Biological Sciences
in the Laboratory

Sixth Edition

Ronald S. Mollick

Department of Organismal and Environmental Biology

Christopher Newport University

Academx
Publishing Services

PREFACE

Welcome to the Biology laboratory! This laboratory course is designed to meet one of the requirements of the Liberal Learning Core Curriculum. One of the Liberal Learning Areas of Inquiry is "Investigating the Natural World." This Area of Inquiry requires students to successfully complete two lecture classes and one laboratory class. The laboratory class must be related to one of the lecture classes taken. To use Biology 109L to help complete this requirement you **must** be currently enrolled in or have already completed one of the following: Biology 107, 108, 111, 112, 113, 114 or 115.

This laboratory class is designed to provide experiences regarding how science works using biological examples. Most of the exercises will teach you about one of the important areas of biology and then provide you with the opportunity to design your own experiments that you and others in your lab group will perform in a later lab session. Learning about the scientific method is therefore an essential part of this laboratory experience.

Your best bet for success in this class is to come to lab fully prepared to engage in science. That means that you should have already read the lab exercise as well as any associated appendices. In addition, you will be expected to have visited any on-line sites included in the lab exercise. And don't forget to bring a flash drive with you to lab. You will not need it for all lab exercises, but be sure to have one available.

These lab exercises will let you experience science as it really is: investigative, educational and goal-oriented. You will learn to ask scientifically based questions and to design experiments that will let you address your questions. You will learn how to treat the data you generate and how to report results both orally and in writing.

I also hope you gain a new appreciation of the value of the scientific way of thinking and have some fun along the way.

ACKNOWLEDGEMENTS

This edition of *Biological Sciences in the Laboratory* was modified with aid from Professor J. Derek Loftis, who is the Biology 109L coordinator. His spirit and ideas, not to mention his sharp eye for grammar and expression, helped considerably. Also, past lab coordinator, Professor Ted Hoagland, was instrumental in modifying earlier editions of this book.

TABLE OF CONTENTS

LAB 1. INTRODUCTION TO THE BIOLOGICAL SCIENCES

I. Science and Biology

Why do people enroll in college? The answers to this question are myriad, but one answer is that they want to become educated people. But what does it mean to be educated? Educated people have developed an understanding of the world around them. There are, of course, many ways to view our world. By completing the Liberal Learning Core, you will have been exposed to most of the important ways in which the world can be viewed. One of those ways is through the use of science.

But what is science? Science can be defined as a method, an approach, a way of doing things. Note that this definition makes science an "action" concept. Your science textbook is not science, but it is the product of scientific thought. The scientific method itself is a method that relies upon observations of the natural world, and the natural world only. It is a method that generates facts about the natural world through use of our senses (sight, hearing), or by using machines that we build to extend our senses (microscopes, telescopes, atomic absorption spectrophotometers).

> **Science defined**: 1. The observation, identification, description, experimental investigation, and theoretical explanation of natural phenomena. 2. Methodological activity, discipline, or study. 3. An activity that appears to require study and method.

It is then the job of the scientist to explain those facts. What scientists try to do is to fit those facts into explanations called theories. The theories explain the facts but these theories, if they are scientific theories, must offer *natural* explanations of the facts and not supernatural explanations.   The theories are, therefore, supported by the facts. If new facts are generated they may fit nicely into the general framework of the existing theory lending more support to that theory. But if the facts do not support the theory, then the theory must change. The theory might have to change slightly, or it may have to be discarded and a new theory formed. As a result of this process, the work of science never ends as new facts are being generated constantly.

Theory defined: A system of assumptions and accepted principles which can be used to explain certain phenomena and which are based upon systematically organized knowledge.

Biology is one of the natural sciences as are, for example, physics and chemistry. Biology is defined as the *science of life*, or, the *study of living things*. Biologists study all aspects of the living creatures including how they are structured, how the structures function, interactions among the creatures and with the environment, reproduction and how traits are passed from one generation to the next, and origins and evolution of the creatures.

This laboratory class is designed to present you with the opportunity to learn how biologists do science. Laboratory exercises are not intended to present a comprehensive look at all major biological processes, but to **expose you to scientific methods as used by biologists**. By completing these exercises, you will come away with an understanding of how science works (the **process** of science), as well as gaining knowledge about certain biological processes.

Remember, products of science and scientific thought are all around you. Educated people need to be able to recognize not only the importance of those products, but the importance of the method that brought us those advances.

TO DO: As a first task, list some of the products or advances of science and scientific thought that you encounter in your life:

II. Scientific Methods

There are many ways to explain how science is done and these explanations illustrate the "scientific method." All scientists use some form of this method to learn about the natural world. Here are the main parts of the scientific method:

A. OBSERVATION AND QUESTIONING

As stated above, all science begins with observations. We look around us and see things. Some of those things we simply accept ("...hmmm, the sun rose in the east today," or, "The leaves of that tree are changing from green to a bright yellow") and we move on with our lives. People with a scientific bent may go further and ask a question about what they saw ("I wonder why the sun rises in the east every day?" or "...why are those leaves changing color?"). Someone who wants to utilize the scientific method takes another step. They decide to try to discover the answer to their question. That leads to the next step.

B. THE HYPOTHESIS

If the question is to be answered, it must first be stated in such a way that it can be addressed scientifically. What this means is that the question must be asked in a way that can be answered, or can be approached experimentally. This operational question is the "hypothesis" which is basically a ***testable guess*** about the observation. In addition, it is usually possible to formulate and test more than one hypothesis.

> **Hypothesis defined:** An explanatory proposition tentatively assumed in order to draw out its logical or empirical consequences and so test its accord with facts that are known or may be determined.

Curiosity about the leaf color change might be turned into hypotheses that say:

1. Green pigments are at a lower level in the leaves that are undergoing color changes from green to yellow than in the leaves that are still green, or (another possible hypothesis follows)

2. Green pigments are at the same level in all leaves, but yellow pigments are greater in the leaves changing from green to yellow.

Note that both of these hypotheses can be tested in a lab (presuming you knew or could learn how to test for pigment presence, which is a standard procedure).

What about the next hypothesis?

3. Green pigments are decreasing because invisible fairies surreptitiously remove some pigments each evening.

There is a problem with hypothesis "3" because we don't have a machine that can test for the presence or absence of fairies or can measure what they might do. As a result, this hypothesis is not testable and is therefore not a scientific hypothesis. The lesson here is that *in science, hypotheses you construct must be testable* so that you can gather information that will allow you to accept or reject the hypothesis.

C. THE EXPERIMENT

The planning stage prior to doing an experiment is when you decide on the methods and techniques you will use to try to address your hypotheses. Here you will decide exactly what you will do and how you will do it. You should also realize, as you set up your experimental protocols, that collecting more data is better than collecting less data. That is, include some **replicate**s in your protocol. Replicating an experiment 3-5 times or more (depending on time and equipment availability) will help you to understand how the organisms typically respond to your experimental protocol. Replicating your work and using averages or mean responses in your data analysis will help you account for natural variation. So, one experimental observation is not enough evidence to determine whether to accept or reject your hypotheses.

One more aspect of good experimental design is the use of **controls**. A control is an experimental constant, against which experimental variables are compared. For example, if you wanted to learn about the effects of a new drug on a particular disorder, you would eventually test it by giving it to experimental animals or people with the disorder (clinical trials) and noting any differences among the groups. But you would need to have a control group, that is, a group not given that drug. The control group would be treated exactly the same way as the experimental group, but no drug.

Then, you could compare the experimental groups (with the drug) to the control group (no drug). Without a control, you would not know if the results you are seeing were caused by the drug, or would have happened anyway. Again, *the control is necessary as a basis of comparison* for experimental work.

> **Control Group:** a standard for comparison with one or more experimental groups. The control group should be identical with the experimental groups *except* for the one variable being investigated.

However, some kinds of scientific work are not experimental and would not have a control. For example, some scientists make observations of natural events or objects from the natural world. The study of animal behavior in nature does not necessarily include controls, although later field and lab experiments may be controlled. Astronauts returned to Earth from the moon with many samples that were studied intensively in laboratory settings. Characteristics of the moon rocks were determined in studies that did not include controls. Paleontologists find and study fossils without the use of controls.

Experiments that you will do in this class will most likely include parts that are referred to as the **independent variable** (IV) and the **dependent variable** (DV). The **IV** is the variable that is controlled and manipulated by the experimenter; whereas the **DV** is not manipulated. Instead, the DV is observed or measured for variation as a presumed result of variation in the IV. For example, you might wish to test the effect of temperature on baking time of cookies. You would manipulate the baking temperatures for several batches and note how long it took those batches to bake. Temperature would be the IV and baking time would be the DV. That is, baking time (the DV) is dependent on temperature (the IV).

Lastly, scientists must examine or analyze the data generated to see if the hypothesis is acceptable or not. So, in science, we create a hypothesis, test the hypothesis, and then examine the data to determine if we can *accept* the hypothesis or *reject* the hypothesis. **Note that we do not "prove" or disprove" the hypotheses.**

D. Evaluating the Data

The work you do in lab will produce **data**. The data will need to be analyzed and then presented in a written and/or oral format. Your data presentations are your results. Exactly how data are treated is dependent on the type of data that have been produced. Your instructor will provide expectations and information on data analysis for any projects that you do. But in all cases, you will want to present the results in an easily readable format. This may include the use of **tables** (rows of numbers or lists of events or characteristics), or **figures** (bar graphs, line graphs, drawings, pictures). In all cases, the tables or figures should be <u>clearly and succinctly labeled</u>. The labels should contain enough information so that the reader knows what the figure or table is about without having to look elsewhere in the report. The figures and tables should also all have a <u>number</u> ("....see Figure 1"), and a <u>title</u> ("Figure 1. The effect of snowball size on the incidence of bloody noses."), and the <u>axes **must** be labeled</u> with both descriptive words and unit type (for example, "Height in cm").

> **Data** defined: 1. information, especially information organized for analysis or used as a basis for a decision; 2. numerical information in a form suitable for processing.

The horizontal or "X" axis would be labeled "Snowball Diameter in Centimeters," and the vertical or "Y" axis would be labeled "Number of bloody noses". Since the number of bloody noses is dependent on snowball size, bloody noses are referred to as the **dependent variable** and goes on the vertical axis. Snowball size is the **independent variable**.

E. Using the Data to Address the Hypothesis

Like every other scientist, you must try to understand what the results, generated from the data, tell you. Examine your results closely. Your instructor may have particular requirements about data analysis that will at least involve the calculation of mean values or the use of other, simple statistics. Use those data analysis techniques to decide whether the results support your hypothesis (and you *accept* the hypothesis) or whether the results do not support the hypothesis (and you *reject* the hypothesis). But what if the results are unclear? What if you are not sure whether or not you should accept or reject your hypothesis? In the world of science, statistical tests, utilizing the laws of probability, can be used to help you make such decisions. Your instructor may show you how to do this with your data.

III. ESTABLISHING HYPOTHESES AND EXPERIMENTAL DESIGN

A. CURING A DISEASE USING THE SCIENTIFIC METHOD

In the course of history, mankind has confronted many challenges. Among them were a number of extremely debilitating diseases, like the bubonic plague, which killed tens of millions of Europeans in the Middle-Ages. Another disease is **pellagra**, which causes skin rashes, mouth sores, diarrhea and mental deterioration or dementia. It was first described in 1735 by a Spanish physician and first reported in the United States in 1902. It soon appeared in epidemic proportions in the southern part of the USA.

Watch the video presentation (about 10 minutes) about pellagra and note how the scientific method was used to investigate and eventually cure pellagra. This video is part of a NOVA series titled "Science Odyssey" which presents the people and discoveries of twentieth century science and technology. The part you will see is from part A, "Matters of Life and Death." This video is also available on youtube:

http://tinyurl.com/ocnc6gy

QUESTIONS (Your instructor may want you to turn in this page)

1. Why did Dr. Goldberger suspect that pellagra was not an infectious disease?

2. What was his hypothesis? Were there any weaknesses in his hypothesis?

3. Why was pellagra found mostly in the southern regions of the USA? And why was it so prevalent in orphanages and prisons?

4. <u>How</u> did he attempt to test his hypothesis (i.e. what were his methods?)

5. Were there any weaknesses in his methods (consider the "scientific method")?

6. What did his results show?

7. How did the scientific community <u>and</u> the public react to his findings? Why?

8. After publishing his results, what did Dr. Goldberg expect? What happened?

9. What was the most important thing you learned from the video?

B. CONSTRUCTING HYPOTHESES AND PLANNING AN EXPERIMENT

It usually takes some practice to be able to construct a hypothesis and to decide how to test it. This exercise will give you practice in doing both of these things. You will **work as a group** with others at your lab table. <u>Your Instructor may require that you hand in your group result.</u>

PROCEDURES

1. Each table of four students will be given one or two statements or situations with which to work. Based on what you are assigned, you must formulate a testable hypothesis whose results can answer significant questions about the information given. Your instructor will give each group a statement or rough hypothesis with which to work. It is the job of your group to both

    a. formulate a <u>testable hypothesis</u>, and

    b. <u>construct an experimental design</u> to test the hypothesis.

You have about 15 minutes for this task. Use Form 1 which is provided on the next page.

2. After your group has developed an experimental design, you will exchange your hypothesis and the experimental design (Form 1) with another group in the class. You now have 10 minutes to evaluate that experimental design. Use Form 2 for evaluation notes.

3. After the 10 minute evaluation period, pass Forms 1 and 2 back to their original group.

4. Now each group will <u>present a short oral report</u> on their plan including a response to the criticisms noted in Form 2.

Your instructor may wish to summarize basic principles of experimental design.

ASSIGNMENT 1. HYPOTHESIS AND EXPERIMENTAL DESIGN

ROUGH HYPOTHESIS OR SITUATION AS GIVEN **AND** TESTABLE HYPOTHESIS:

EXPERIMENTAL DESIGN (USE AN OUTLINE FORMAT, NOT A NARRATIVE)

ASSIGNMENT 2. EVALUATION FORM

1. Was the hypothesis well stated? If not, suggest new wording.

2. Are the variables properly described? If not, suggest wording.

3. Are there an adequate number of replicates? Controls? If not, suggest changes.

4. Does this experiment adequately test the hypothesis? If not, what needs to be changed?

ASSIGNMENT 3. *SIMBIO* VIRTUAL LABS

We will be doing two general types of lab exercises this term. The first is a hands-on style where you will be designing experiments and manipulating equipment. The second type is a virtual lab done entirely on a computer. The latter lab type is produced by *SimBio*. On their website they have introductory versions of the software that we will be using later in the semester.

Go to their website and examine an introductory version of two of the labs we will be using. The basic idea is to familiarize you with a style of laboratory exercise that will be used later in the course.

Here is the link:

http://tinyurl.com/qzonavq

Click on the "Darwinian Snails" box on the right and then view the demo video. When the video finishes, you can then run the video clip for the "Nutrient Pollution" lab which can be accessed on the right of this screen.

LAB 2. HANDS ON VARIATION

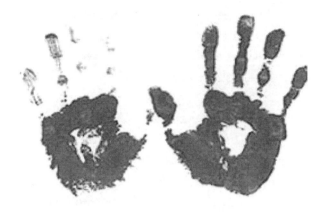

Human beings have existed as a species only about 200,000 years. We are a young species and have not had much time to evolve. Since variations accumulate over time, one might expect that not very many variations would have accumulated. If space aliens landed on our planet, they might concur with that idea and note that *Homo sapiens* look much more alike than different. However, the human genome, which comprises the entire complement of genetic material located in the chromosomes, includes about 3 x 10^9 base pairs of DNA and the extent of our variation is such that no two people, except identical twins, ever have been or will be exactly alike. We are individuals. But all humans have a great deal of their genetic information in common. It is these similarities that define us as a species. While we exist in many populations, our species is one continuously variable interbreeding group.

Our traits are passed on to the next generation when we reproduce. But prior to that event, a process called **meiosis** (see the text box on the next page) mixes our genetic content as our gametes are formed in our gonads (ovaries or testes). This process results in the formation of eggs or sperm whose genetic properties are new. When eggs are fertilized by sperm cells, the resulting human embryos are genetically different from every other embryo.

In some cases we can trace the flow of genes from parent to offspring and even through families. In those cases, if you know which genes the parents have you can predict which traits the children are likely to get. Conversely, if you know which traits the children have, you can predict which genes their parents have. Such knowledge is based upon the understanding of the science of genetics, first established by Gregor Mendel in the 19th century.

> Meiosis is a divisional process that occurs in certain cells in the gonads (ovaries or testes). This process reduces the chromosome number of those cells by half. As a result of meiosis, the cells produced have exactly 23 chromosomes each, which is half of the normal number, 46. Then, when gametes develop from these cells, they each have half the normal number. That is, they are **haploid**. When fertilization occurs, two haploid gametes merge to form a cell, the zygote, which now has the full number of chromosomes. That is, the zygote is **diploid**. Once this zygote starts to cleave, to form the early embryo, each subsequent cell produced will be diploid with the full, normal number of human chromosomes: 46. Without this reductional division, setting up a later fusion of gametes, chromosome number in offspring would be abnormal.
>
> But an additional thing happens in meiosis. As the cells in the gonads divide, their chromosomes swap parts. That is, they **synapse** (line up with other chromosomes that look alike = **homologous chromosomes**) and then **crossing over** occurs, where chromosomes exchange parts. As a result of the swapping of chromosome parts containing genes, the gametes end up being different genetically. Later, when egg meets sperm, the resulting embryo is genetically different from every other embryo ever formed.

The Mendelian Genetics Appendix at the back of this exercise details some of that work and the basic principles underlying inheritance of a single gene pair or what is known as **monohybrid inheritance**. Studying this appendix is critical to your understanding of the next part of the exercise. Be sure to do that before coming to class.

I. HUMAN GENETIC VARIATION

As explained above, we are all very much alike. Studies indicate that the DNA of any two individuals is 99.9 percent identical. That 0.1 percent is where we vary from one another. This seems like such a small amount, but it is obviously very significant. It is within this small fraction of the genome where we find the phenotypic differences that distinguish each one of us from all others. We can demonstrate one of those phenotypic differences quite easily.

PROCEDURE

1.   Your instructor will pass out pieces of paper that have been impregnated with the chemical PTC. Hold on to it until your instructor tells you what to do. This chemical is found in the Brassica family of vegetables, such as cabbages, brussel sprouts and kale. Some people can taste this harmless chemical, but for others it is tasteless. Your ability to taste (or not) is determined by the presence or absence of certain genes (see Table 1). Once everyone has a piece of the paper, give it a try. Touch it lightly to your tongue for a few seconds and you will soon know if you carry the genes for tasting PTC.

QUESTION: 75% of people can taste this chemical. Did the class data approximate this number? Why or why not?

PROCEDURES

1. Use the information in Table 1 to identify various phenotypes. Write in your own data and then collect class data as well.

2. Calculate what the genotypes of your parents might be for the listed traits. Put the results in Table 2.

QUESTIONS

1. About 70% of us can roll our tongues. How close did class data come to this expected frequency? Some evidence indicates that tongue rolling can be learned. How does that effect any conclusions?

2. About 75% have free earlobes. How did class data compare?

3. Only 25% have hitchhikers thumb. How did class data compare?

16

Table 1. Human phenotypes and genotypes.

TRAIT	DESCRIPTION Phenotypes	GENETICS Genotypes	YOU Phenotype & Genotype	CLASS DATA Phenotypes
1.Widow's Peak	Hairline dips down to a point in center of forehead	Dominant trait (W_); a continuous hairline is recessive (ww)		
2.Dimpled Cheeks	Cheek indentation on one or both sides	Dominant trait (D_); absence is recessive (dd)		
3.Tongue rolling	Ability to roll tongue into a trough or U	Dominant trait (U_); inability is (uu)		
4.Attached earlobes	Earlobe is continuous with face	Recessive (aa), if earlobes swing free it is dominant (A_)		
5.Long palmer muscle	Form a fist with your hand and clench it; observe inside of wrist; if you can see three tendons stand out you have a long palmer muscle	Recessive (mm); if you see only two tendons then the third is missing and you have the dominant gene (M_)		
6. Freckles	Pigment spots on the face	Freckles are dominant (F_); lack of freckles is recessive (ff)		
7.PTC taste	Ability to taste the chemical phenylthiocarbamide (harmless)	Tasting is dominant (P_); non tasting is recessive (pp)		
8.Bent little finger	When hand is laid flat, little finger bends in toward ring finger	Dominant trait (F_); if little finger is straight, recessive (ff)		
9.Mid-digital hair	Presence of hair on second segment of both your 3rd and 4th fingers	Dominant trait (H_), absence of hair is recessive (hh)		
10.Hitchhiker's thumb	Thumb curved back excessively when hand spread in extended position (>60°)	Dominant trait (L_); regular thumb is recessive (ll)		

Table 2. Parental genotypes for listed traits.

TRAIT	LIKELY PARENTAL GENOTYPES	TRAIT	LIKELY PARENTAL GENOTYPES
1.Widow's Peak		6. Freckles	
2.Dimpled Cheeks		7.PTC taste	
3.Tongue rolling		8.Bent little finger	
4.Attached earlobes		9.Mid-digital hair	
5.Long palmer muscle		10.Hitchhiker's thumb	

II. HAND VARIATION

Many animals have grasping appendages but, scientifically, true hands are only found within the mammalian order Primata (the primates—lemurs, tarsiers, monkeys, apes and humans). A true hand also features an opposable thumb, which can be rotated 90° so as to touch any of the tips of the fingers. The human hand has 27 different bones, and lots of muscles and tendons which are necessary to allow the grasping and holding of items so necessary to our way of life.   In this section, you will examine hand data retrieved from students in Biology lecture and laboratory sections. We have hundreds of hand drawings, with associated information. The hand drawings will allow you to measure hand spans, and to detect other hand characteristics like hitchhiker's thumb, mid-digital hair, and bent little fingers. In addition, the sex and height of the person can be found on each form.

It is your job to try to learn about variation in human hands by assessing various hand characteristics.

PROCEDURES

1. First, add to the database by tracing your hand on a blank data sheet and filling in other information. Be SURE to stretch out your hand completely before tracing.

2. Now you and your group must decide what to study. Write several hypotheses that you can test by assessing hand data sheets.

3. Then, plan an experimental regime, and choose, with the aid of your instructor, two hypotheses to test. Your instructor may want you to turn in this information so that it can be returned, with comment, at the start of the next lab session.

4. You will test those hypotheses at the next lab meeting.

5. Ask your instructor about your responsibilities regarding data analysis. Your instructor may want you to use the information in Appendix 4 on Data Analysis.

6. A lab report may be required, due the following lab meeting:

Date due _____

7. You may also be expected to report on your project to the class. Appendix 2 covers how to write and to orally present a report. Your instructor may provide additional information on this.

III. DNA EXTRACTION

We know that genetic traits are bound up in the structure of the DNA molecules that are found within the chromosomes that are located in the nucleus of every cell. What follows is a procedure that will allow you to actually see DNA and without even using a microscope! You will extract DNA from strawberries, and what follows is how to do it.

QUESTIONS

1. What do you think the extracted DNA will look like?

2. Will you be able to see genes?

3. What, really, is a "gene"?

PROCEDURES

1. Obtain a Ziploc bag and one strawberry (frozen strawberries may be used). If the strawberries are small, use two of them.

2. Remove any stem material and anything green from around the berry.

3. Place the strawberry in the bag, zip it closed, and smash and grind it with your fingers for about two minutes. Try you best not to break the bag!

4. Obtain 10 ml of **extraction buffer** from the side of the room. The buffer contains chemicals that will break apart protein chains that bind the DNA, and will also dissolve any lipids (fatty molecules). The buffer is actually made from dishwashing detergent, salt and water, so don't worry about chemical burns).

5. Add the extraction buffer to the plastic bag and close the bag.

6. Kneed the contents of the bag for about a minute, which will allow the chemicals in the buffer to work on the strawberry pulp.

7. Now obtain a funnel, a paper filter and a small beaker or test tube. Insert the paper filter in the funnel, put the funnel in the beaker or tube, and then pour the contents of your bag into the funnel and let it drip into the beaker. You can now dispose of the filter and whatever pulp remains.

8. Next, go to side of the room and obtain about 20 mls of alcohol. This can be either ethyl or isopropyl (rubbing) alcohol and slowly pour it into the beaker or tube. This will cause the DNA to precipitate out of the solution (i.e. the DNA will change form into a solid).

9. At the top of the beaker you should now see what looks like white scum. Using a flat toothpick or other available implement, dip it into the scum and remove it from the contents of the beaker or tube by rotating the implement. This is your strawberry DNA!

You can also watch a **youtube video** showing this process:

http://tinyurl.com/nv529uq

QUESTION: How is DNA extraction actually used in real life?

APPENDIX -- MENDELIAN GENETICS.
A VERY SHORT COURSE

In lab, you have been asked to consider certain obvious human genetic traits like the presence or absence of attached earlobes, PTC tasting, and tongue rolling. These traits are apparent or not based upon the presence or absence of certain genes. Today, we know that the genes present on the chromosomes in the nucleus of cells, made of DNA, and are responsible for holding the information to build the traits. The traits are then passed from one generation to the next via reproduction. People who study this process are studying heredity, or the science of genetics.

Genetics is a relatively new science dating back to the work of an Austrian monk, Gregor Mendel, in the 1850s. Mendel taught science and math at the monastery, but also was known for his beautiful gardens. Few people at that time knew that he used his gardens to study how certain traits were passed from generation to generation in pea plants. He called these traits "discrete hereditary units," which were later referred to as "genes." He studied seven characteristics of the pea plants as they were passed from generation to generation such as flower color and plant height. As Mendel followed traits from generation to generation, he noticed that certain outcomes with certain ratios always appeared. For example, when he crossed pure bred plants that always produced white flowers with pure bred plants that always produced purple flowers, the hybrids (next generation = F_1 generation) always produced purple flowers. The white trait was not apparent. Then, when he crossed the purple flowered hybrids with each other, the plants of the following generation (the F_2 generation) *always* produced three purple flowered offspring for every white flowered offspring. Being a mathematician, he was intrigued with this information and hypothesized a biological system that could produce such ratios. He decided that certain things must happen if those ratios were to consistently appear. Here are the basic elements of his plan.

1) Each parent contributes one gene for each trait in its gametes, so that after fertilization, the offspring ends up with two genes for each trait, one from each parent (i.e. the gametes are haploid, but the offspring are diploid).

2) The individual genes that the parent contributes via the gametes are derived from pairs of genes in the cells of the parental gonads; when these gametes are formed in the gonads the gene pairs separate (that's meiosis, though Mendel was not actually aware of this process) so each gamete has one gene of each gene pair = haploid state; this was Mendel's "theory of segregation."

3) Any gene pair in the gonads is sorted out for distribution within gametes independently of other gene pairs. This is Mendel's "theory of independent assortment," meaning that what happens to one type of gene has no influence on what happens to another type of gene.

Mendel's work on pea plants serves as the basis for genetics. Some of his terminology, or modern equivalents of his terminology, are still in use today. For example, it was noted in the flower color example (above) that the plants in the F_1 generation all produced purple flowers. The white trait was not expressed. The purple trait is referred to as the **dominant** trait, while the white trait is the **recessive** trait. But the white trait reappeared in the F_2 generation, showing that it had not disappeared, but sometimes was not expressed. Mendel also realized that there were two separate genes for this trait (let "P" = the dominant purple trait, and "p" = the recessive white trait). These are "alternative forms of the same gene", which is a definition of the word **alleles**. In this case, there are two forms of the flower color genes (two alleles: P for purple flower color, and p for white flower color).

Mendel had assumed that each trait was governed by a pair of genes. In the flower color example, the two alleles are P and p. Each individual's gene pair for this trait is some combination of these two genes. That is, individuals have a **genotype** for the trait that consists of two genes. An individual could be **homozygous** for the trait, where both genes are of the same type. In this example, the homozygous genotype would be either "PP" or "pp." The plant could also be **heterozygous** for the trait, where the heterozygous genotype contains one gene of each allele (= "Pp"). All of the plants in Mendel's studies contained one of those three possible genotypes relative to flower color: homozygous dominant (PP), homozygous recessive (pp), or heterozygous (Pp). The word "genotype" always refers to the specific gene content. If you want to state a genotype, then it would be in the form of the letters that represent the genes. In this example, the genotypes available are PP, Pp, and pp. One additional term is **phenotype**, which is a descriptive word, based upon what the trait looks like to your eye. There are two phenotypes in the flower color--

purple and white. However, based on genetic content, a flower with the purple phenotype could be one of two different genotypes: either PP or Pp. Visually, you would not be able to tell the difference. The white flowered phenotype has only one possible genotype: pp.

If you are monitoring how single gene pairs are passed from generation to generation, you are studying "monohybrid inheritance." The flower color example is a case of monohybrid inheritance, as are the human genetics traits you have been asked to assess in the laboratory. You can visually do genetic crosses and predict their outcome through the use of the Punnett-square, when the genotypes of the parents are known. Table 1 illustrates the use of a Punnett-square for the P_1 cross (PP x pp) discussed above. The Punnett-square is a mathematical tool that allows you to show the allele(s) of the parental gametes and all possible gene combinations for those gametes in the offspring of the next generation. The gametes are haploid and the offspring are diploid. The results from the Punnett-square also illustrate the proportion of each offspring type one can expect.

Table 1. Punnett-square showing a P_1 cross of pure bred purple flowered plants (PP) with pure bred white flowered plants (pp). The gamete types are represented by single letters (P or p), while the offspring (members of the F_1 generation) are in the shaded areas of the table and have two letters (Pp) to represent their diploid genotype.

PP x pp

Gamete types of each parent are shown in the top row and left column.	P	P
p	Pp	Pp
p	Pp	Pp

Note that the contents (shaded area) of the Punnett-square show that the members of the F_1 generation all have identical genotypes (Pp). The phenotypes of these plants with regards to flower color will all be purple based upon the dominance of the purple gene (P). The white phenotype does not appear, although the gene for white (p) is present in each individual. It is not expressed as a genotype because it is recessive. The only way a white phenotype can be expressed is if a plant is homozygous for the white trait (pp).

Table 2 shows a Punnett-square for the outcome of a genetic cross among members of the F_1 generation (Pp x Pp). These individuals have a heterozygous genotype and all produce purple flowers. The shaded contents of this Punnett-square represents the F_2 generation. Again, note that the shaded contents of the square illustrate 1) all possible genetic combinations for these parents, and 2) the proportion of each genotype that is predicted.

Table 2. Punnett-square showing a monohybrid F_1 cross of heterozygous offspring with each other (Pp x Pp). The gamete types are represented by single letters (P or p), while the offspring (members of the F_2 generation), are in the shaded areas of the table and have two letters (PP, Pp, or pp) to represent their diploid genotype.

Pp x Pp

Gamete types of each parent are shown in the top row and left column	P	P
P	PP	Pp
p	Pp	Pp

The outcome of this cross as illustrated in the shaded area of Table 2 shows that the F_2 generation is expected to have three different kinds of genotypes (PP, Pp, and pp). Because of dominance, there will be only two phenotypes (purple and white). Remember, the Punnett-square is used to predict proportional outcomes. These results would allow us to expect, therefore, that in the F_2 generation

1) the ratio of expected genotypes in the offspring is 1:2:1; that is, one PP for every two Pp and one pp (or, 50% = Pp, 25% = PP, and 25% = pp), and

2) three of four offspring (75%) will have a purple phenotype and one of four offspring (25%) will have a white phenotype.

If you understand the principles and examples used, you should also be able to work backwards and predict possible parental genotypes if you know the genotype of the offspring. For example, if the offspring is homozygous dominant (PP) then you know that it must have received one "P" gene from each parent. Each parent's genotype must, therefore, have at least one "P" gene to give. Parental genotypes of this nature could be PP or Pp. The two parents each must be one of these.

Mendelian genetics is an important basis of research in genetics. Scientists who study human genetics and especially genetic disorders must be well grounded in its basic principles. Modern genetics, including molecular genetics, DNA and biotechnology are grounded in basic Mendelian genetics. Many genetic disorders are each attributed to single genes, which are distributed among people based on Mendelian principles. The National Institute of Health (NIH) has a web site devoted to Mendelian inheritance in people. Visit this site to learn more about human genetics:

http://www.dnaftb.org

A SHORT GLOSSARY OF GENETIC TERMS

Alleles............... Alternative molecular forms of the same gene, as in the two genes for flower color, "P" and "p."

Diploid.............. When a cell has the full, normal complement of chromosome pairs; in people, that is 23 pairs in the nucleus of each cell (= 46 chromosomes total in each cell)

Dominant.............A dominant gene will express its phenotype when present and is typically represented by an upper case letter, like "P."

F_1 generation......Literally means "first filial generation," or first generation offspring, produced from the first parental generation (P_1).

F_2 generation......"Second filial generation," or second generation of offspring, produced from F_1 generation parents.

Gametes............. These are the haploid sex cells: sperms and eggs.

Gene.................A "discrete hereditary unit", said Mendel, or, a sequence/section of DNA on a chromosome that holds the information to build a particular trait.

Genotype.............This refers to the particular alleles that are carried; use letter designations when describing them.

Haploid...............A haploid cell has one chromosome of each chromosome pair, which means that it also carries one gene of each gene pair. In people, gametes are haploid, carrying 23 chromosomes.

Heterozygous...... When alleles of a gene pair are different (as in "Pp").

Homozygous........When alleles of a gene pair are identical (as in "PP" and "pp")

Hybrids...............They are offspring from a cross between two true breeding individuals and which have inherited nonidentical alleles for a trait ("Pp" in the F_1 generation is a hybrid).

Meiosis................A cell division that occurs in specialized cells in the gonads (ovaries and testis) which requires two sets of divisions, and results in four cells, each of which are both haploid and genetically different. These cells later become gametes which are haploid.

P_1 generation........The parental generation.

Phenotype.......... This is the observable trait that is based upon the genes being carried (such as "purple" or "white" flower color).

Recessive.............A recessive gene is not expressed if it is paired with a dominant gene (as in "Pp"). The recessive trait is only expressed if the gene pair is homozygous recessive (as in "pp"). The recessive gene is typically represented by a lower case letter ("p").

LAB 3. SWEATING, SPORTS DRINKS AND BIOLOGY

Life is out to get us. If we don't watch out and pay attention, we could get into serious trouble. For example, many of us like to keep active. Jogging, working with weights, stretching, walking, plus sports like basketball, tennis, golf and Frisbee-tossing are all things that can help us keep fit. We also know that during those activities we not only tone our muscles and use stored energy, but we also lose fluids and minerals that should be replaced. That is, we sweat. This is great, because when the sweat evaporates off the surface of the skin, it carries away heat and we feel cooler. If the day is hot, we can lose a significant amount of fluids (up to 3L per hour in trained athletes) and minerals to the point where we could even feel sick, develop heat stroke, or worse. So, we drink to replace what we lose.

Physiologists and others concerned about human health need to understand how the cells in our bodies work in order to offer the best advice and to produce or recommend the best replacement regime. Some of that advice includes the use of sports drinks of various brands. Manufacturers of such drinks have teams of physiologists who study the mechanisms of fluid and mineral replacement. They also have teams of advertising executives who try to convince us that we would be better off consuming their products than simply drinking water. Replacing lost fluids, they say, happens faster with the sports drinks than just consuming plain water. Is that really so? See the Appendix, **Gatorade Speaks**, at the end of this exercise.

Today in lab you will have a chance to plan hypotheses and a testing regime relating to that supposition. But first, you must understand the basic mechanisms that govern mineral (or *solute*) flow, and water (or *solvent)* flow into and out of cells. Remember, we each consist of billions of cells that are all affected by these important mechanisms: **diffusion** and **osmosis.** Unless we understand what these mechanisms are and what factors influence them, we will be unable to approach our topic scientifically.

I. DEFINITIONS AND EXPLANATIONS: DIFFUSION AND OSMOSIS

Both of these processes refer to the movement of *molecules* or *ions* (ions = charged atoms, like Na+, sodium). In the example above, the sweat consist of the <u>solutes</u> (the minerals in the sweat) and the <u>solvent</u> (the water in which the minerals are dissolved).

SOLUTE = the substance dissolved in the SOLUTION; in biological systems, the solution is typically water.

The water consists of many millions of water molecules, H_2O. The solute consists of millions of, for example, salt molecules (NaCl and other things) dissolved in the water. Those salt molecules will quickly disassociate into charged atoms like sodium ions (Na^+) and chlorine ions (Cl^-). Once we swallow fluids, they move into the digestive system, and then into the circulatory system where they are transported to all the cells. But how do they get out of the digestive system and into the cells? The water molecules are constantly vibrating with kinetic energy, which tends to move any solute molecules in the water from areas of high solute concentration to areas of low solute concentration. That is, the solute molecules move because of the actions of the

---

DIFFUSION: "The <u>passive</u> movement of molecules or ions from areas of greater concentration of those molecules or ions to areas of lesser concentration of those molecules or ions." In nature, <u>nutrients</u> diffuse from the soil into plant roots, allowing growth. Oxygen diffuses into the gills of fish from the water in which they swim, and into our lungs from the air we breathe; CO_2 diffuses out.

---

kinetic energy that originated from the sun. The solute molecules do not contribute any energy or motive force—they are passive riders. This is the essence of diffusion.

So, solutes typically diffuse out of the digestive system and into the circulatory system where they encounter the cells. In creatures, solutes are constantly diffusing **into cells** (such as nutrients of various types), and **out of cells** (like wastes). Of course, for any solute to move in either direction, they must be able to pass through the cell's membrane. Our sweat glands actively push out fluids onto the skin's surface. But this is an <u>active</u> process requiring energy expenditure and does not involve diffusion, which is a passive process. When we try to replace those lost fluids by drinking, the sugars and salts (solutes) and water (the solvent) get into cells by the mechanism of diffusion.

But there is a <u>special type of diffusion</u> that must be considered. This type of diffusion is called *osmosis* and, when considering biological systems, <u>only</u> applies to the water molecules. Water molecules also diffuse. When they diffuse through a selectively permeable membrane (one that always allows water molecules through, but may limit solutes), it is called **osmosis**. Water molecules also will only move from areas of greater concentrations of water molecules, to areas of lesser concentrations of water molecules. When they do that through a cell membrane, then it is referred to as osmosis.

OSMOSIS: "The diffusion of water molecules (or other solvents) through a selectively permeable membrane." <u>Water moves by osmosis from the soil into plant roots</u>, keeping plants healthy and supplying the water needed for a number of functions including photosynthesis. <u>Water moves into our cells by osmosis</u> after we drink it.

However, the concentration of solutes on the two sides of the membrane will influence the **direction of water molecule movement**. If solute concentration is higher on one side of a membrane (call it side "A"), that side is said to be "**hypertonic**." "Hyper" means high; in this case, high solutes. The other side of the membrane (side "B") where the solute concentration is low is termed "**hypotonic**." "Hypo" refers to the low solutes on side "B." In this case, **water molecules** will tend to move from side B, the hypotonic side, to side A, the hypertonic side. More specifically, this would be from areas of low solute concentration and high water concentration (side B) to areas of high solute concentration but low water concentration (side A). If both sides of the membrane have exactly the same water/solute concentration, then both sides are "**isotonic**" to each other (iso = same). See the text box on the next page for additional information. **Knowing how to use this terminology will be necessary when explaining the results of your experiments.** Figure 3-1 illustrates what happens to plant cells (with cells walls that animal cells lack) in varying solutions. See further explanation in the <u>text box</u> on the next page.

Figure 3.1 Plant cells in hypertonic, isotonic and hypotonic solutions. Water enters and leaves the cell at the same rate in an <u>isotonic</u> solution leaving the cell size and weight unchanged. In a <u>hypertonic</u> solution, more water leaves the cell than enters it and the plasma membrane pulls away from the cell wall as the cell shrinks, loses weight, and becomes plasmolyzed (note that the cell walls are stiff and will not swell or shrink much). In a <u>hypotonic</u> solution, more water enters the cell than leaves so the cell gains water, the plasma membrane swells and becomes turgid. It also gains weight.

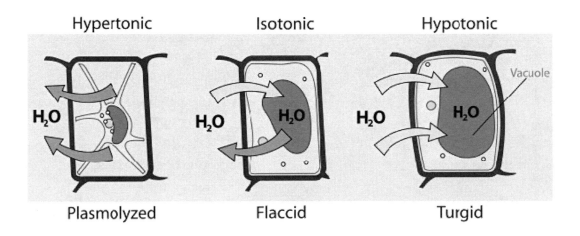

Hypertonic, Hypotonic, Isotonic and Which Way the Water Goes

If cells are placed in fluids that are **hypertonic** to the cells, there will be a natural tendency for solutes to move into the cells (diffusion), and for water molecules to move out of the cells (osmosis). If that happens, the cells will shrink and lose weight. It is the loss of the water molecules from the cells by osmosis that directly affects the cell's weight.

If cells are placed in fluids that are **hypotonic** to the cells, there will be a natural tendency for solutes to move out of cells (diffusion), and for water molecules to move into cells (osmosis). If that happens, the cells will expand and gain weight due to adding water molecules. Cells with weak membranes or which lack cell walls can even burst.

If the cells are placed into an **isotonic** solution, then water and solute molecules will move in both directions at an equal rate and there will be no change in the weight of the cells.

II. TEMPERATURE INFLUENCES ON THE RATES OF DIFFUSION AND OSMOSIS

Like all physical processes, the rates of both diffusion and osmosis can be affected by a number of factors. Today you are going to examine the effects of temperature on diffusion. Next week you will have an opportunity to test hypotheses regarding the effects of sports drinks and other solutions on diffusion and osmosis.

Changing temperatures in and around cells will affect the rates of diffusion. In this experiment, you will observe how different temperatures affect diffusion using gel tubes of agar to represent cells. You will drip a specific amount of a chemical, sodium hydroxide (NaOH), onto the gel in the tube. The NaOH will disassociate which produces invisible OH$^-$ ions. As these ions diffuse into the yellow gel a color change will occur. This color change is really related to pH changes in the gel as the OH⁻ ions diffuse. You can measure the rate of diffusion by measuring, in millimeters, the distance the color change travels over time. You will be using three different temperatures: room temperature (_____ ºC), 55ºC, and 0–4ºC.

State your hypothesis: _____

_____

PROCEDURES

1. Obtain three tubes of yellow gel agar (it contains phenol red, a pH indicator) and mark each for later identification.

2.   Make an ice-water bath by filling a 600 or 1000 ml beaker with ice and then adding cold tap water. Stir. After five minutes, measure and record the temperature of this ice bath using a metal thermometer which you can find at the side of the room.

3. Put one tube in the ice-water bath, one tube in the 55ºC incubator, and leave one tube at room temperature. Let all tubes sit for 10 minutes. This period of _equilibration_ will allow the contents of the tubes to reach the desired temperatures.

4.   After the 10 minute equilibration period, note the time and add precisely six (6) drops of concentrated NaOH to each of the tubes. **Be VERY careful with this chemical**. Sodium hydroxide (NaOH) is a caustic chemical and can cause severe burns. If you spill any on your skin, immediately flush the area with lots of water. Report any spills.

5.   Now quickly return each of the tubes to their proper equilibrated temperature regime. DO NOT leave them out on the lab tables.

6. After 40 minutes, measure the distance in millimeters (mm) from the starting point to the pink/yellow interface using a ruler. Record your data and the data from other groups in Table 3.1. Be sure to record your measurements in millimeters.

7. Calculate the rates of diffusion in millimeters per minute (mm/min) at all three temperatures by dividing the number of mm moved by the number of minutes. Be sure you are using class data for this calculation.

8. Evaluate your hypothesis.

QUESTIONS:

1. Did you accept or reject your hypothesis? _____

2. What is the relationship between temperature and rate of diffusion? _____

3. Why, specifically, does temperature have an effect on the rate of diffusion? _____

Table 3.1. Distance of diffusion in millimeters (mm) after 40 minutes. Be sure you are using class data.

Group Number	0–4°C	20–25°C	55°C
1			
2			
3			
4			
5			
6			
Mean			
Rate of diffusion (mm/minute)			

III. INTERNET DEMONSTRATIONS

OF BROWNIAN MOTION, DIFFUSION AND OSMOSIS

While your tubes are cooking, your instructor may show you or refer you to demonstrations of Brownian motion and diffusion.

1. **Brownian Motion** is a visual demonstration of the molecular activity that drives both diffusion and osmosis. In these applets, the tiny particles can

represent the random movement of air or water molecules (energized by, ultimately, the sun) which are pushing around larger particles like solutes in a solution, or perfume molecules in the air. The link below provides demonstrations and explanations.

http://tinyurl.com/osmkoeq

The Wikipedia article (link below) is long, but just read the first paragraph which provides historical perspective, and then look at the simulations on the right. The molecules are moving quickly, but in real life, water molecules at room temperature move even faster at about 1400 miles per hour!

http://tinyurl.com/yzaqfq

2. Diffusion. The following applet demonstrates how perfume molecules diffuse in air. Click on the grey box to load the applet. Click on "setup" then slide the "ticks" bar to the left of center (to slow the process; the tick bar controls the speed of movement of the air molecules and moving it to the left would represent a decrease in air temperature). Now click on "release perfume molecules" and finally, click on "go/stop" to start the simulation. Repeat to do it again. Note that you can also adjust the number of air and/or perfume molecules. Remember, that it is the action of the air molecules (Brownian motion) that are responsible for moving the perfume molecules and causing them to diffuse. Also note that this applet may not run on a MAC. If so, skip it and use the next link at the bottom of this page.

http://tinyurl.com/c6jsgem

QUESTIONS

1. What is responsible for the movement of the air molecules? Where do they get their energy?

2. What actually moves the perfume molecules? Do they ever stop moving?

This link will take you to a 28 minute program demonstrating both diffusion and osmosis. Lots of information here and some good visuals.

http://tinyurl.com/qammqjy

The following link is a short animated video on diffusion.

http://tinyurl.com/42by8e

3. Osmosis. This applet provides an animated explanation of how osmosis works. Click on "play" and watch the demonstration. Then, answer the five questions.

http://tinyurl.com/5wn3kw

IV.   DIFFUSION, OSMOSIS, SUGAR AND SPORTS DRINKS

Now we have the background to address our questions about sports drinks. You will now create hypotheses and a testing protocol, which you will **use next lab period**, regarding rates of diffusion and osmosis. You will use potato cylinders as models of human cells. Remember, potatoes are parts of living creatures and so are made of many living cells. Even though you will not be doing your experiments until next lab, read through the following procedures to see the materials and general methods that will be available for your use.

PROCEDURES

1. **Review Appendix 5** on the microscope in the Appendices section. Then examine (using stain, a slide and a cover slip) a very tiny, flat piece of potato under the microscope to see the cells which will verify cellular content. **Sketch** these cells. Be sure to wash and dry the slide when finished and then return it to the box. You may discard the cover slip.

2. Think about the sugar content of sports drinks (see the information sheets available in lab) and how that might affect diffusion and osmosis. We also have a range of sugar solutions for you to use (see number 4, below) and diluted orange juice.

3. You will design an experiment choosing among the sugar solutions, sports drinks, diluted juice, and pure water available in lab; you may also utilize temperature as a factor. The oven at the back of the class will be set to 37°C and hot plates and ice will be available.

4. The text box below lists which solutions will be available in lab. Technically, a **solution** is a homogeneous mixture of one or more solutes dissolved in a solvent. Note that the solvent is the substance that is present in the greatest amount. These are **mixtures**, which are substances made by combining two or more different materials in such a way that no chemical reaction occurs.

AVAILABLE SOLUTIONS

1. Diluted orange juice (one part orange juice diluted with three parts water = 25% normal juice).
2. Distilled water (i.e. pure water, no solutes).
3. Sugar solutions (sucrose and water):
    - 1% sucrose
    - 3% sucrose
    - 5% sucrose
    - 10% sucrose
4. Gatorade
5. Homemade sport drink made from: 1 liter of water, one third cup of sucrose (table sugar), one fourth teaspoon of table salt (NaCl) plus flavoring (like unsweetened Kool Aid).

---

5. You will measure osmosis by keeping track of the weight of potato cylinders utilizing the following method:

a. Use a cork borer to cut potato cylinders; these cylinders will be your human cell models. Make the cores by carefully pushing borer through the sides of the potato, and not through the potato lengthwise. Cut the potato skin off the cylinders and cut all cylinders to the same length. Lengths of 4 cm will be good. Be sure to use the same cork borer to create all your cylinders.

b. The number of potato cylinder pieces (plugs) required will vary depending on how you set up your experiment, so consider how many you will need. Remember, good experiments include replicates and controls. Five replicates would be a good number.

c. Rinse the potato plugs in tap water, blot gently, and weigh each one and **record individual weights** (**not** group weights) in grams (until you are ready to use them, cover the weighed plugs with damp paper towels). A blank data table is included in this exercise. This initial weight will be your starting point. What will happen to this weight after exposure to varying environments is an expression of the effects of diffusion and osmosis. Will the plugs in varying environments gain or lose water? How fast? Remember, the potato plugs represent gut cells and the solutions used represent the fluids one can drink.

d. You will create these environments by putting the plugs in 250 ml beakers filled with known, measured amounts of the solutions you have chosen to use, and in the temperature regime you have chosen. The temperature chamber in lab is set to 37°C (**Question**: why was this particular temperature chosen? _____). Be sure to fill the beakers at least two-thirds full of the solutions you are using.

e. Be consistent in the amounts of the solutions you use in each beaker. However, the beakers should be at least two-thirds filled.

f. The beakers must also be labeled so that you do not lose track of their contents. Use a wax pencil for labeling.

g. When you are ready, immerse the plugs into the varying environments you create. Be sure to **note the time**, as you will want the exposure time to be the same for all treatments. The recommended exposure time is 45 minutes. Stir the solutions with cores every 10 minutes using a clean stirrer. Don't cross contaminate by using a dirty stirrer.

6. Be sure to first create a testable hypothesis, followed by an experimental regime. Again, don't forget about replicates and controls. As usual, check this with your instructor before starting.

7. As you finish your experiments, remove the plugs from the solutions, blot and **weigh them individually**. Also take a moment and <u>touch</u> the plugs that have been sitting in the various solutions. Do they feel the same? Why? _____

Be sure to clean the beakers and other pieces of equipment you used with detergent. Rinse thoroughly.

V. ANALYSIS AND PRESENTATION OF DATA AND CONCLUSIONS

Your instructor will specify how your data is to be treated and reported. **Next lab session** it will be your job to explain what you did and why you think things came out the way they did. Don't forget to review Appendix 4 on Data Analyses and Appendix 2 on written and oral reports. Be sure to use one outside reference source when writing your report. See Appendix 3, Finding Academic Resources for additional instructions.

DATA TABLE

You can easily calculate the <u>percent weight change</u> of potato cores by using the following formula:

$$\frac{\text{Final Mass} - \text{Initial Mass}}{\text{Initial Mass}} \times 100$$

APPENDIX -- GATORADE SPEAKS

A question was sent to Gatorade.com by the author of this lab book regarding rehydration. Here is the question and the response:

QUESTION: "Considering rehydration ONLY, isn't the fastest way to get water back into the cells of the body to drink pure water? That is, if one were to drink eight ounces of Gatorade or eight ounces of water, which would produce faster rehydration?"

RESPONSE from ConsumerRelations@gatorade.com (September 30, 2005):

Thank you for thinking of us as a source of information. If we understand your question correctly, considering rehydration only (setting aside electrolyte replacement and carbohydrate benefits) water and Gatorade Thirst Quencher have the same gastric emptying rate. However, cells are not made up of pure water. In order to replace the proper balance of water and electrolytes to maintain blood sodium levels, a properly formulated sports drink like Gatorade is superior to water alone.

Plain water is often not enough for proper hydration. An accumulation of research shows that sports drinks are better for maintaining hydration than drinking water alone. Water "turns off" thirst before complete rehydration occurs. In fact, research shows that people will drink more of a lightly flavored beverage than plain water and therefore will stay better hydrated. Water also turns on the kidneys prematurely so you lose fluid in the form of urine much more quickly. The small amount of sodium in a sports drink like Gatorade—no more than what is in an equal size glass of milk—allows your body to hold onto the fluid you consume rather than losing it through urine.

Water can be a good beverage choice during physical activity, particularly when nothing else is available. But water doesn't contain flavor, carbohydrates, or electrolytes, the stuff that makes sports drinks more effective than water at enhancing performance. It is import to drink fluids with an adequate amount of sodium, particularly for prolonged runs and continued sweat losses. Over enough time, not replacing sodium can cause blood sodium level to fall, thereby increasing the risk of electrolyte imbalance. This can lead to muscle cramps or more severe situations such as hyponatremia, a potentially life-threatening condition.

We hope this information is helpful. If we have misunderstood your question, please feel free to send a more detailed explanation and we will do our best to reply to your satisfaction.

Michael
GSSI

Questions: What do you think?   Do the results of any of your experiments relate to this question and Gatorade's answer?_____

_____

Do your results follow the Gatorade prediction? Why or why not?

_____

_____

To answer the "why or why not" question you **MUST** utilize principles covered in the first lab session.

LAB 4. EVOLUTION AND SNAILS

Evolution is a scientific concept that is the paradigm or underlying framework for all of biology. The word itself means "change." In a biological context it refers to changes in creatures over time. Evolutionary theory helps us to understand the origin and evolution of life on Earth. It also is used to explain many biological events on the biochemical and molecular levels as well as the physiological, morphological and behavioral levels. Evolution is a concept that now is firmly accepted within science although it remains controversial in some segments of our society. Go to the link in the middle of the next page to view a short video on this controversy (Video 7, "Why is evolution controversial?"). The New York Times also has a web site indexing their news articles concerning "the evolution debate":

http://tinyurl.com/88554

How did evolution become an accepted scientific theory? Historically, we know that beginning in about the 16th century, naturalists began to closely examine the world. Scientific inquiry began to blossom, especially in Europe. By the beginning of the 19th century, naturalists began to notice certain consistencies from such diverse areas as comparative anatomy, paleontology (fossil study), comparative embryology (study of developmental events), and geology. They all agreed that 1) the earth and life on earth was not just old, but very old; 2) significant changes had occurred over time not just in geological features, but in the living organisms; and 3) a natural process must have produced the diversity one sees in creatures, both extinct and living.

In 1858, two British naturalists, Charles Darwin and Alfred Wallace, presented a new theory which could be used to explain the evolutionary process. The basic ideas of this theory are still in use today, although the theory has been modified considerably to take new findings into account. But until Darwin and Wallace presented their ideas, scientists lacked a coherent explanation of the changes they saw around them. Today, evolution is considered to be both a fact and a theory. The **facts** include the millions of fossils as well as genetic (DNA), biochemical, developmental and morphological evidence, all of which demonstrates that evolutionary change occurred. In the world of science, there is no doubt that evolution occurred based upon those facts. But **how** exactly did evolution occur? Evolutionary **theory** is the attempt to explain the facts, and the theory changes as new facts are discovered. That is the way of science.

Be sure to go to the following web site to view two short videos titled "How Do We Know Evolution Happens?" and "How Does Evolution Really Work?" Other videos at this web site may also be of interest.

<u>**http://tinyurl.com/yamntj**</u>

I. EVOBEAKER©: DARWINIAN SNAILS

At the end of your lab work, your instructor may require you to turn in some of these pages along with a report; each student must be prepared to do this. **You will need a flash drive to save data for your report so be sure to bring one to lab.** Work through all parts of this exercise. During the next session you will execute your own experimental design. By the end of today you will need to create hypotheses and experimental designs. Part VI addresses these issues, but your instructor may have additional directions.

Evobeaker© is a simulation of an actual evolutionary event. The simulation demonstrates how natural selection can operate on populations of marine snails that live in intertidal areas on the northeastern coast of the United States. This work is based upon actual research done by Dr. Robin Seeley, which was published in 1986 by the National Academy of Sciences (*Proceedings of the National Academy of Sciences, USA* 83: 6897-6901). Dr. Seeley's research and this simulation demonstrate how natural variations are acted upon by natural selection to change population characteristics. That is, **this work demonstrates evolution in action**. After running the first five parts of the simulation, part VI will allow you and your group to do your own independent research. At that point, you must create hypotheses, decide how you will test them using the tools of the simulation, then test the hypotheses, gather data, and write a report based on your work. Your laboratory instructor will provide more explicit information as to exact requirements.

In general, this simulation demonstrates the effects that a newly introduced predator, the European green crab, *Carcinus maenas*, has on shell thickness of the intertidal flat periwinkle (a snail), *Littorina obtusata*. You can learn more about green crabs by following the link below.

http://tinyurl.com/ndhdsyv

The following link will take you to more information about the flat periwinkle, *Littorina obtusata*:

http://tinyurl.com/qjl2r4r

Now it is time to begin the Darwinian Snails simulation. Be sure to read the instructions carefully before you do anything. Do all steps in order. That way, you will learn how to operate the simulation and will later be able to design your own experiments.

Darwinian Snails

Prelude

The flat periwinkle is a small snail that lives on seaweeds growing on rocky shores in New England. Among this snail's enemies is the European green crab. As its name suggests, the European green crab is not native to North America. It traveled to the East Coast from Europe early in the 19th century. Before 1900, the green crab did not occur north of Cape Cod, Massachusetts. After the turn of the century, however, the crab expanded its range northward, and is now found as far north as Nova Scotia. The crabs' range expansion introduced a new predator to periwinkle populations north of Cape Cod.

44

Biologist Robin Seeley suspected that New England's periwinkle populations had evolved due to predation by green crabs. Seeley found, in a museum, periwinkles collected in 1871 at Appledore Island (north of Cape Cod). She compared these old shells to new shells she gathered herself at the same place. Seeley measured the thickness of each shell. Her data appears in the tables below.

Shells collected in 1982-4, eighty years after green crabs arrived

14	11	12	14	9	11	12	13	14	10	14	10	14	12	13
10	15	13	14	15	15	13	15	11	16	12	18	16	16	17
17	17	15	12	13	15									

Shells collected in 1871, before European green crabs arrived

5	8	1	9	4	8	8	8	11	3	9	8	7	8	5
8	8	13	9	10	9	5	2	8	7	5	9	8	8	5
11	12	8	3	3	5	9	8	6	7					

Each number represents a single shell. (Don't worry about the unit of measure. Seeley plotted her data as the logarithm of thickness, which have been converted to integers.) Bigger numbers mean thicker shells.

Plot the data for the shells collected in the 1980s on the top grid at the right. If you're working with a partner, one of you should read the number while the other places an X on the grid for each shell. An X has been put on the grid for the first shell (with a thickness of 14); you add the rest. When you have more than one shell with the same thickness, stack the Xs on top of each other.

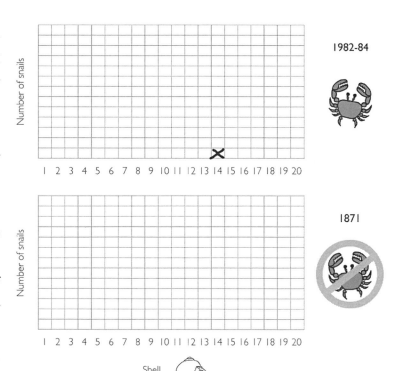

Next, plot the data for the shells collected in 1871 on the bottom grid on the previous page. The graphs you have just drawn are called **histograms**. Histograms are a powerful way to summarize the variation among individuals in a population, and to compare populations to each other.

On the top histogram you just drew, showing the periwinkles from the 1980s, **mark the average shell thickness of the snail population with a triangle as has been done at the right**. Don't do any calculations; just judge the average by eye. This is the point at which your collection of Xs would balance. **Also mark the average thickness of the 1871 periwinkle population.**

Q1. Which snail population has the larger average shell thickness, the population from 1871, or the population from the 1980s?

On the histogram showing the periwinkles from the 1980s, **mark the range of variation in thickness among the snails with a two-headed arrow as has been done at right**. For the collection of Xs at right, the range of variation is 6 units. Also mark the range of variation in thickness among the periwinkles from 1871.

Q2. Which snail population has the **larger range** of variation in shell thickness?

Note that the average shell thickness and the range of variation in shell thickness are properties of a **population** of snails, not properties of any single individual. There may not be any individual snails whose shell thickness is exactly equal to the average, and no individual snail has a range of variation in thickness. Only a group of snails, taken together, can have an average and a range of variation.

Recall that Robin Seeley had predicted that the flat periwinkle population on Appledore Island would have evolved between 1871 and the 1980s. Like *average* and *range* of variation, *__evolution__* is a term that applies to population parameters of organisms, not to any single individual. Evolution is reflected by a change in the composition of the population; it is typically seen as a change in the average and/or the range of variation.

Q3. Was Seeley's prediction correct? That is, are the average shell thickness and/or the range of variation in thickness different for the 1980s snail population versus the 1871 population?

Compare your histograms to the histograms in the illustration below (reprinted from Seeley, 1986), which we have drawn from Seeley's data. As the graphs and photos in the illustration show, the snail population on Appledore Island in the early 1980s was, indeed, dramatically different from the snail population that was there in 1871. The snails had, on average, shells that were thicker than those of their ancestors. The 1980s population also showed a somewhat lower range of variation in shell thickness. The flat periwinkles living on Appledore in the early 1980s were descendants of the snails that were living there in 1871. **We can therefore describe the change in the population as descent with modification, or evolution,** albeit small-scale evolution.

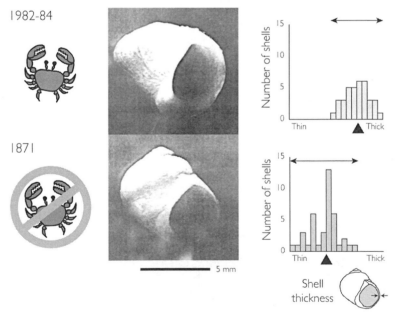

How did this descent with modification, this evolution, happen? The **mechanism of evolution** is the subject of this exercise. You will do experiments on a model population to explore how evolution works. Then you will return to Seeley's flat periwinkles to see how the model applies to them.

Part 1: A Model of Evolution by Natural Selection

1) Launch the Simbio Virtual Labs program. Select "Darwinian Snails" from the EvoBeacher Labs option on the right of the screen.

2) You will see a population of snails scattered around the Coastline on the left. Take a closer look at these snails by double-clicking (or control-clicking) on one of the snails. A window pops up showing you an enlarged view of that snail and the thickness of its shell. Examine at least 9 other snails in this way and **make note** of the shell thicknesses.

> **Q4.** Which shell thicknesses are the most common? Which are the least common?

3) Look at the histogram on the right side of the screen. This sorts the snails on the coastline by shell thickness, and shows the number of snails in each category.

> **Q5.** Are the proportions of snails with different shell thicknesses in the histogram similar to the sample of snails you examined in 2) above?

4) You will now become a European green crab. You will feel especially crabby if you are not getting enough to eat, and the best snacks available on the coastline are these tasty looking snails. All you have to do is crack their shells by pounding on them with your claw. Get your claw ready for action by clicking on the CLAW MODE button (in the control panel, the button with the claw on it). You are now officially a European green crab.

5) Before beginning your feast, **COPY** the histogram of shell thicknesses and save it in a text document. To do this, click on the **COPY** tool to the left of the **REPRODUCE** button (the two sheets of paper icon in the control panel). Then click on the histogram of shell thicknesses. This will copy the histogram into your computer's clipboard. Now reduce Evobeaker and open a new document in Word and use the paste command in the "edit" menu to drop the histogram into the document. Label this graph *Part 1: Starting Population* so that you remember what the snails looked like before you got to the Coastline.

6) But before beginning your feast, make a prediction (i.e. **construct a hypothesis**).

     Q6. What do you think will happen to the shell thickness distribution in this population of snails as you eat some of them?

    Hypothesis:

7) Start the simulation by clicking on the far left arrow button in the Control Panel on the bottom of the screen. The snails will start to crawl around. There are initially 50 snails, as shown by the *Current Snail Pop* item below the Coastline.

8) Find a snail you want to eat and start clicking on it (you have already clicked on the CLAW button to activate the function). When you claw at it enough times, the shell will crack, you'll eat what's inside, and the snail will disappear. The **Current Snail Population** will also show that there is one fewer snail around.

9) Notice the **Crab Happiness Score** below the Coastline. This score will go up every time you eat a snail, but it will go down every time you click on a snail with your claw without finishing the snail, because the more effort it takes you to get your meal, the "crabbier" you become. The coastline started with 50 snails, and it takes 25 snails to fill you up. Keep eating snails until you have eaten close to 25 (so there are about 25 remaining), and try to get as high a *Crab Happiness Score* as possible while doing this.

    Q7. Do you notice any differences in the histogram of shell thicknesses at this point compared to the starting snail population? If so, <u>explain</u> why this change happened.

10) If you—the crab—goes away for a while after your big meal, then the snails have a chance to reproduce. Stop the model by clicking on the STOP button (the square button in the Control Panel). Then make the snails reproduce by clicking on the **REPRODUCE** button on the right side of the screen.

11) Each of the surviving snails makes two new snails by cloning, and then dies. Unlike most real snails, there is no mating. Each baby is identical to its parent. To see this, switch back to the **SELECT** button (the standard mouse arrow in the Control Panel, next to the **CLAW** button) and double-click on a few pairs of snails (twin children of a single parent). You should see that the shell thickness is the same in both snails in each pair.

12) You are hungry again! Start the model running by clicking on the GO button, click back on the **CLAW** button so you can eat again, and have another meal of 25 snails. Don't forget to try to keep your *Crab Happiness Score* as high as possible by eating your snails with the fewest clicks possible.

13) Digest your meal and let the snails reproduce again by clicking on the **REPRODUCE** button. Then have one more meal of 25 snails. At the end, **REPRODUCE** once more so you finish with about 50 snails.

14) When your third meal is done, **COPY** the histogram of shell thicknesses and paste it into your text document. Label it *Part 1: Generation 4.*

15) Compare the starting histogram you saved earlier to the fourth-generation histogram.

    Q8. Has the distribution of shell thicknesses changed as you hypothesized or predicted in 6)? Explain:

16) Playing crab may become tedious after a while. To prevent you from becoming frustrated, *EvoBeaker* will let you add crabs to the Coastline. These crabs will eat snails automatically while you watch. To do this, first click the **RESET** button in the Control Panel (the backwards arrows icon to the right of the STOP button). This will let you start over with a new population of snails. **COPY** the histogram of shell thicknesses and paste it into your text document. Label it *Part 1: Before Crabs.*

17) Now you will add crabs to the mix by using the **ADD CRITTER** icon to the right of the crab claw which currently shows a snail. Click *and hold* on the

down-pointing arrow head to the right of the snail. A crab icon will appear below the snail icon. Slide the cursor onto the crab icon and release the mouse button. Now, each click of the mouse will add a crab. Add three to five crabs to the coastline.

18) Run the simulation (with the **GO** button) and watch the crabs as they eat snails. Keep an eye on the size of the snail population. **STOP** running the simulation when there are 25 snails left (get as close to 25 as possible).

19) **COPY** the histogram of shell thickness and paste it into your text document. Label it *Part 1: After Crabs*. Compare your before crabs and after crabs histograms.

> **Q9**. Which snails tended to get eaten? Which snails tended to survive?

20) Click the **REPRODUCE** button to let your snails reproduce. Run the simulation until only 25 snails are left, then stop it. Click the **REPRODUCE** button again, run the simulation until only 25 snails are left, then stop it. Click the **REPRODUCE** button one more time.

> **Q10**. How does the evolution of the snail population when predatory crabs are present compare to the evolution of the snail population when you acted as predator?

Part II: The Requirements for Evolution by Natural Selection

You saw the snail population **evolve** (= change over time) as a result of predation which is one form of natural selection. What is required for such change to take place? This section of the lab exercise explores several conditions that affect whether the population will change as individuals are selected.

A. Variation

1) What if all the snails started out the same? Could the population still evolve? To get a uniform population of snails (no variation in shell thickness), click on the **Shell thickness is variable** checkbox on the right part of the screen so that it is <u>unchecked</u>.

2) To get a new population of snails, reset the model by clicking on the RESET button in the control panel at the bottom of the screen.

3) Switch to *Select Mode* (click the arrow button next to the claw button). Look at the shell thickness of a few snails. Also look at the histogram of shell thickness.

> Q11. Is there any variation in shell thickness among the snails now?

4) Use the **COPY** tool to copy the shell thickness histogram from the screen, paste it into your text document, and label it *Part 2: No Variation – Starting Population*.

5) Make a prediction (**create a hypothesis**) – do you think this population of snails will evolve as predators start eating them? Explain why or why not.

> Hypothesis:

6) Now test your hypothesis. Switch back to *Add Critter Mode* by clicking on the button with the whole green crab on it. Add three to five crabs to the Coastline. Start the model running (with the **GO** button) and let the crabs eat about 25 snails.

7) Stop the model and let the snails **REPRODUCE**. Copy the histogram from the screen, paste it into your text document, and label it *Part 2: No Variation – Generation 2*.

Q12. Was there a change in the distribution of shell thickness among the snails? Explain **why** this is different than when you or the crabs were eating snails before.

Q13. **Why** does the distribution of shell thickness stay the same now, even though predators were eating just as many snails?

B. Inheritance

In your last experiments, the shell thickness of each snail was identical to that of its parent. Shell thickness was completely genetically determined, so each snail inherited the genes for shell thickness from its parent and ended up with a shell of exactly the same thickness. What if that weren't so? What if shell thickness was not heritable—if there were no genetic basis for shell thickness— but each snail instead grew its shell to a random thickness that had nothing to do with its parent's shell? To find out, click on the *Shell thickness is heritable* checkbox on the right side of the screen so it is unchecked.

1) Put variation in shell thickness back into your model by clicking on the *Shell thickness is variable* checkbox so that it is checked again.

2) Reset the model. **COPY** the histogram from the screen and label it *Part 2: No Inheritance – Starting Population*.

3) Before starting the simulation, see what will happen during reproduction by clicking on the **REPRODUCE** button. Using *Select Mode*, look at a few pairs of snails.

Q14. Do the offspring have the same shell thicknesses as the parents (are the snails identical within each pair as before)?

Q15. Do you think that the distribution of shell thickness in the population will change over several snail generations as predators start eating snails? Why or why not?

4) **RESET** the model again so that you start with 50 snails as before. Now switch to *Add Critter Mode* and add three to five crabs. Run the simulation until there are just 25 snails left.

5) **REPRODUCE**, and then let your crabs have two more meals, reproducing after each one.

6) **COPY** the new shell thickness distribution from the screen, paste it into your text document, and label it *Part 2: No Inheritance – Generation 4*.

Q16. Why are the starting and ending shell thickness distributions so similar to each other, even after your crabs had three meals of the thinnest-shelled snails?

C. Selection

Imagine a crab that is especially large and can crack snail shells no matter how thick they are. This crab just takes snails to eat randomly, without any preference for thinner shells. Will there still be a change in the distribution of shell thickness over time? To test this, click on the *Survival is selective* checkbox on the right of the screen so it is unchecked.

1) Make shell thickness heritable again by clicking on the *Shell thickness is heritable* checkbox. Both the top two boxes should now be checked, and only *Survival is selective* should be unchecked. You should also see a button called **EAT RANDOM SNAIL** that has become active next to the **REPRODUCE** button.

2) **RESET** the model and start it running. Do not add crabs. Click the **EAT RANDOM SNAIL** button a few times and watch what is happening to the snails in the Coastline. You will see that each time you click **EAT RANDOM SNAIL**, one randomly-chosen snail disappears. You'll see both thin-shelled and thick-shelled snails disappearing with equal probability.

3) **RESET** the model. **COPY** the histogram from the screen, paste it into your text document, and label it *Part 2: No Selection – Starting Population*.

54

Q17. Do you think the distribution of shell thickness in the population will change over time as your super-crab starts having meals? Why or why not?

4) Start the model running and eat 25 snails by clicking on the **EAT RANDOM SNAIL** button 25 times. Have the snails reproduce, and have two more meals, reproducing after each. To speed up the process of eating random snails, you can change the way the button works to eat more than one at a time. Click the number "1" to the immediate right of the **EAT RANDOM SNAIL** button, and select "25". Then click the button one time, and you will instantly see 25 randomly selected snails disappear. **REPRODUCE**, have one more meal of 25 snails, and then **REPRODUCE** again.

5) Copy the histogram from the screen, paste it into your text document, and label it *Part 2: No Selection - Generation 4 - Trial 1*.

Q18. Was there a change in the distribution of shell thickness among the snail population? Is this what you expected? Explain.

6) Reset the model.

7) Repeat steps 4) and 5), copy and label the next histogram *Part 2: No Selection - Generation 4 - Trial 2*.

8) Reset the model and repeat steps 4) and 5) once more, labeling the histogram *Part 2: No Selection - Generation 4 - Trial 3*.

9) Look at all three *Generation 4* histograms with no selection.

Q19. Are there changes in the shell thickness distribution from the initial pattern?

EvoBeaker™-Darwinian Snails   Copyright 2009 by SimBio Software for Teaching and Research, Inc.

Q20. Are these changes consistent in all three of your trials?

10) Try to explain any changes you observed in the populations. Consider whether the changes happen for the same reason as the changes in distribution in Part 1 of this lab (between 5 and 15). You might also think about whether the changes, either in Part 1 or in this section of Part 2, could have happened just by random chance.

Explanation:

NOTE: In 9), the mechanism of evolution is not natural selection. It is called *genetic drift*.

Part III: Darwin's Theory of Evolution by Natural Selection: The Conditions for Evolution

Here is how adaptive evolution happens. Darwin said that:

A. If a population contains variation for some character, *AND*

B. if the variation is at least partly heritable (differences among individuals are at least partly due to differences in the genes they have inherited from their parents), *AND*

C. if some variants survive to reproduce at higher rates than others,

THEN the distribution of that character in the population will change over time.

Condition C, nonrandom survival and reproduction, is called **natural selection**. The individuals that survive to reproduce are said to be *naturally selected*. Together, the three conditions and the conclusion are **Darwin's Theory of Evolution by Natural Selection**.

1) Using the data from your experiments, describe the conditions under which the snail population will evolve toward thicker shells and the conditions under which it won't. Refer back to your notes and the histograms you saved as evidence.

Part IV: The Source of Variation Among Individuals

In all the experiments you have done so far, your starting population contained individuals of seven different shell thicknesses. In later generations, some of the thicknesses may have disappeared from the population, but no new shell thicknesses appeared. In real populations, where do new variations come from? The answer is **mutations**. For our present purposes, a mutation is an error during reproduction. That is, while most offspring may resemble their parents, an occasional mutant offspring will possess some different characteristics and not completely resemble the parents.

1) To see the role of mutation in evolution, select *Mutation's Role* from the *Select An Exercise* menu at the top of the screen.

2) The snails in this new stretch of Coastline have shells up to a thickness of only 4, without the 5, 6, and 7-thickness snails on the last area of Coastline. There is now a *Reproduce with Mutation* box in place of the checkboxes in the last screen, and it is currently not checked so there are no mutations. As before, add three to five hungry crabs to the Coastline. Let your crabs eat three meals of 25 snails each, letting the snails reproduce in between meals.

Q21. Is there a limit to how far predatory crabs can drive shell thickness in the snail population? Why or why not?

3) Now click on the checkbox *Reproduce with mutation* so that it is checked.

4) Let the snails reproduce. Before you start the model again, use the **SELECT** tool (arrow) to examine some pairs of snails.

Q22. Are the offspring usually identical to each other (and to the parent)?

Q23. Are there cases where one of the offspring is different from the parent?

Q24. If so, is the change usually towards a thinner shell, a thicker shell, or is it equally likely to be towards either one?

If the answer isn't clear from this reproduction, look at this again the next time you reproduce and then come back and answer this question.

5) Let your crabs eat at least five more meals of 25 snails, letting the snails reproduce in between. (You can speed the process by just clicking the **REPRODUCE** button when the snail population drops to 25; you don't have to stop the simulation. The snails will reproduce, and the crabs will keep right on eating.)

Q25. Can you drive the population further towards thicker shells now (with mutations) than you could before (without mutations)? Explain how this can happen, even though there are just as many mutations towards thinner shells as towards thicker shells.

Part V: What Makes A Population Evolve?

Reflect on your experiments with the model snail population and consider the following issues:

Q26. After they were born, did the <u>individual</u> snails ever change their shell thickness or color? If the individuals didn't change, how was it possible for the population to change?

Q27. Did snails grow thicker shells because the snails <u>needed</u> them in order to survive? Does "need" affect evolution and natural selection? Is "need" part of Darwin's conditions for evolution? If not, where did new thicknesses come from?

Q28. What role did the predators play in causing the population of snails to evolve? Did they create a need for the snails to change – a need to which the snails responded? Or did the predators simply determine which snails survived to reproduce and which didn't?

Part VI: CHALLENGE – Evolution by Natural Selection in Flat Periwinkles

Robin Seeley hypothesized that the flat periwinkles of Appledore Island evolved in accordance to Darwin's Theory of Evolution by Natural Selection. When the green crabs arrived, they started eating the thin-shelled snails. This left only the thick shelled snails to reproduce. And when the thick-shelled survivors reproduced, they had thick-shelled offspring. The end result is that the composition of the population changed. Thin-shelled snails became rare, and thick-shelled snails became common.

Seeley performed two experiments to test her hypothesis. In the lab, Seeley offered each of 8 crabs a thin-shelled snail. All 8 crabs quickly crushed and ate their snails. It took them an average of 42 seconds. Seeley offered each of another 8 crabs a thick-shelled snail. Only one of these crabs was able to crush and eat its snail within 8 minutes. During that time many of the other 7 crabs gave up trying.

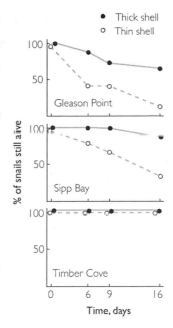

In the field, Seeley drilled small holes in the shells of a number of snails, and used fishing line to tether the snails to seaweeds in the intertidal zone. She then returned every few days to see which snails survived. This method allowed Seeley to distinguish between snails that were killed by crabs, part of whose crushed shells remained tied to their tethers, versus the few snails that broke free of their tethers or died in their shells. She tethered the snails in pairs, with each pair including one thin-shelled snail and one thick-shelled snail. Seeley tethered 15 pairs at Timber Cove, where crabs appear to be absent; 15 pairs at Sipp Bay, where crabs are present but rare; and 15 pairs of snails at Gleason Point, where crabs are common. She checked on the snails after 6, 9, and 16 days. The <u>results</u> appear at the side of this page (reprinted from Seeley, 1986). Filled circles represent snails with thin shells; open circles represent snails with thick shells.

1) Review the requirements for evolution by natural selection.

> **Q29.** What evidence, if any, does Seeley have that the flat periwinkles of Appledore Island vary in the thickness of their shells?

> **Q30.** What evidence, if any, does Seeley have that snails with thick shells are more likely to survive than snails with thin shells? Think carefully about this.

Q31. What evidence, if any, does Seeley have that shell thickness is heritable? (Again, think carefully about this.)

2) Seeley's data provides direct evidence that two out of three of Darwin's conditions for evolution by natural selection are true of the flat periwinkle population on Appledore Island. For the third condition, the evidence is indirect at best.

Q32. For which of the three conditions is the evidence you have seen the weakest? Explain.

The remainder of this section is a slightly more advanced (and fun!) section of this lab. Please check with your instructor to see if this last part is included in your assignment.

Your challenge now is to **conduct your own independent research** using more biologically realistic models of snail populations. **You will do this independent research during the next lab session.** However, work through this section so that you will see what tools are available for your use.

You will work with a snail population that has lived in a crab-free environment for several generations, and a snail population that has lived in a crab-infested environment for several generations. Your charge is to design and complete observational studies and experiments to address three questions: **i)** Do the snails from the crab-infested environment have thicker shells, on average, than the snails from the crab-free environment?; **ii)** Do the snail populations meet all three requirements for evolution by natural selection?; and **iii)** Do the snails from the two environments differ because one or both has evolved by natural selection, or do they differ simply because snails can smell crabs and grow thicker shells when they need them?

The next few steps give you new tools that you can use in your research: small enclosures that you can use for controlled experiments; the ability to place snails with certain shell thickness in those enclosures; and crabs whose claws are bound shut with rubber bands. Using these tools, you will gather data and then write a short paper describing your results and conclusions.

Snail Tanks

3. Select *More Snails* from the *Select An Exercise* menu. You will see the screen change to include two stretches of coastline: West, which lacks crabs, and East, which has crabs. You can answer research question(s) simply by looking at the histograms on the right side of the window. Note that these histograms show the *proportions* of the shell thickness categories and not actual numbers. Also, don't forget to copy, save, and label any histograms you plan to present later as evidence. Below the coastlines, you will also see four experimental tanks that don't contain anything at the moment.

4. Run the model for a while to see that the snails in these populations have all the features of real life snails. They vary in shell thickness and experience occasional mutations. They reproduce sexually and can do so without your help. You will see juvenile snails appear with a blue color to indicate that they are not yet mature. These snails grow up and mature. Eventually, they will die of old age.

5. To move a snail into one of the experimental tanks, click on the SELECT button (the arrow button). Then click and hold down the mouse button on a snail that you want to move. Drag that snail into the tank and let go of the mouse. You will see the snail dropped into the enclosure, and it will be gone from the coastline. This ability to move snails around will let you arrange specific matings, if you want to. Just drag two adults to an experimental tank, make sure they are overlapping each other a bit, and run the model.

6. You can add a crab to a tank by either dragging a crab from one of the coastlines, just as you do with the snails, or by adding crabs using the *Add Critter* tool as you did in Part III of this lab.

Gathering Populations of Snails

7. Depending on your experiment, you may want to have a variety of different shell thicknesses in a tank, or you may want to have many snails all of the same thickness. You can set up either of these situations by dragging snails of the thickness you want from the coastline into the tanks. If you want to drag many snails at once, first stop the simulation and then hold down the shift key while you click on one snail after another. All the snails you click on will get a color tint to show that you have selected them. Then, click and hold the mouse button down on one of the selected snails, and drag it to a tank. The rest of the selected snails will follow along.

8. You may want to add juvenile snails to your tank to see whether or how their shell thickness changes as they mature. To do this, select the smaller, blue snails from the coastline. You will have to double-click (or option-click) on each one to see its shell thickness at the time you select it. You may want to record these thicknesses in order to see whether they change by the time that snail becomes adult.

Scent-of-Crab

9. Snails may be able to sense the presence of crabs, for instance by smelling them or seeing them, and then respond to their presence. You may want to see whether snails respond to the crabs without actually letting the crabs eat any snails. You can do this by putting rubber bands around the crab's claws so the crabs cannot actually eat a snail. To get a crab with its claws rubber-banded shut, click and *hold* your mouse on the **ADD CRITTER** tool (the down-arrow head button with a picture of a critter next to it -this is just to the left of the trash can). When the pull-down menu pops up, select the crab picture with red bands over its claws. Then click once in an enclosure to add a single crab with bound claws.

You As Scientist

Using the tools described above, you can answer the remaining research questions:

• Do the snail populations meet all three requirements for evolution by natural selection? (You may want to focus in particular on the requirement that was least-strongly supported in Seeley's research.)

• Do the snails from the two environments differ because one or both has evolved by natural selection, or do they differ simply because snails can smell crabs and grow thicker shells when they need them?

Design and carry out one or more experiments to generate your data, and then write a short paper that includes your methods, results, and conclusions. **Do not forget about the use of controls and replicates.**

NOTE: For one biologist's follow-up on Seeley's work, see the paper by Geoffrey Trussell listed in the bibliography.

Bibliography

Seeley, Robin Hadlock. 1986. Intense natural selection caused a rapid morphological transition in a living marine snail. *Proceedings of the National Academy of Sciences, USA* 83: 6897-6901.

Trussell, Geoffrey C. 1996. Phenotypic plasticity in an intertidal snail: The role of a common crab predator. *Evolution* 50: 448-454.

LAB 5. SCIENCE AND WINE

I. INTRODUCTION

Wine and other fermented beverages have been made by man for at least seven thousand years, dating back to early Neolithic times. Historically, fermented beverages have often been preferred over water since they were safer than water (no water born diseases due to the alcohol content) and provided more nutrition than water. In addition, alcoholic beverages were a social lubricant and their manufacture could be important to the local economy and to cross cultural trade. Of course, the well known psychotropic effects of alcoholic beverages can became a sought after side effect, which can end up being harmful to human health.

Wine making relied upon the presence of wild yeast cells (actually, living creatures in the Kingdom Fungi) found naturally on the skin of grapes. It is these living yeast cells

> ### 5.1   Mechanism and Vitalism
>
> In the 19th century, scientists and philosophers debated why things happened in cells, including the fermentation process. The *mechanists* thought that everything could be explained in mechanical (the stomach as a grinder) or chemical terms. The *vitalists* believed that within living organisms was a "vital spirit" which was responsible for doing many things which could not be duplicated in a laboratory. That is, life was something special and not amenable to laboratory duplication.
>
> Scientists could be found on both sides of this issue, including Louis Pasteur, the famous French scientist (pasteurization process), who was a vitalist. He was sure that the transformation of fruit juice to wine was a marvelous process that could not be done outside a yeast cell. He and other vitalists were crushed when, in 1898, Edward Buchner isolated an enzyme from yeast and used it to make alcohol. So, fermentation, this "vital" reaction was shown to be just another chemical process.

66

that cause alcoholic fermentation and produce wine. When grapes were crushed and placed in closed containers, the mash would show evidence of bubbling (CO_2 production), ethyl alcohol would form, and the flavor would change. After straining the mash, and perhaps aging it, the mixture was drinkable and more nutritious than water.

Wine making, in the latter part of the 19th century, became part of an interesting scientific and philosophical debate (see text box 5.1). However, it was not until the 20th century that scientists learned about the function of the fermentation process. That is, they learned how yeast cells benefited from this process. In general, the function of alcoholic fermentation in yeast and other cells that do this is to manufacture numerous molecules of a high energy chemical compound (adenosine triphosphate or **ATP** for short) that can be used by any number of cellular processes as an **energy source**. Without ATP, cells could not accomplish much. The CO_2 and alcohol are simply byproducts or useless (to the yeast) waste products of the fermentation process accomplished by the yeast cells. Of course, we use the yeast and the CO_2 produced to make

5.2 Aerobic and Anaerobic Cellular Respiration

Our cells must have a source of energy to survive. In order to manufacture the ATP they require, cells first take in high energy compounds entering from the digestive system and distributed by the circulatory system. These molecules are derived from the foods we eat. But these molecules are too complex to be used directly as an energy source. Our cells, utilizing enzyme systems found first in the cytoplasm and then in organelles called **mitochondria**, are able to convert these compounds to various forms. As the compounds form, energy is released which is then used to make the ATP. This process requires oxygen gas; i.e. it is **aerobic**. Remember, the main waste products of this process are CO_2 and H_2O.

But not all cells require oxygen gas. Bacteria (Kingdom Monera) as well as some single celled creatures (Kingdom Protoctista) plus some forms of plant (Kingdom Plantae) and animal (Kingdom Animalia) cells can manufacture ATPs without oxygen; i.e. they are **anaerobic**. **Alcoholic fermentation**, as discussed, is an anaerobic process whose function is to manufacture ATPs for yeast cells, with alcohol and CO_2 produced as waste. **Lactate fermentation** can occur in our muscle cells when oxygen gas is absent. The products are, of course, ATP, but also lactate or lactic acid which produces that burn or dull ache we feel when exercising strenuously. Lactate bacteria (*Lactobacillus*) make their ATPs in a similar fashion. When we mix those bacteria in with milk the commercially important end result is cheese or yogurt.

But don't forget that the **function** of all these processes in the various cells is to manufacture ATPs for use. It is fortunate that some of the byproducts are useful to us.

bakery products rise, and to manufacture alcoholic beverages. The alcohol that is mixed in our gasoline is also derived from this process. These are significant economic importances. Fermentation only occurs in the absence of oxygen gas (O_2) and is an anaerobic process. A different process that requires oxygen gas (aerobic cellular respiration) occurs in most cells, including human cells. It, too, functions to make ATPs for the cell's use. See text box 5.2 for more information about anaerobic and aerobic cellular respiration and fermentation.

If you want to make good wine, you must understand the factors that affect the process. These would be things like temperature, pH (how acidic or basic is the mash), type of yeast, grape variety, and others. You would also need to find a way to measure the fermentation process so that you can know what the effects of the variables might be.

This lab exercise is designed to run over three lab periods. The first lab period is when you will learn how to measure fermentation and will also design your own experiment which you and your lab group will do next time. The third lab period will be devoted to presentation and discussion of the results.

II. HOW TO MEASURE ALCOHOLIC FERMENTATION

Today, you will learn how to measure this process. In general, you can measure any process by measuring what goes into the process, or by measuring the products of the process. We will be measuring alcoholic fermentation today by measuring the amount of one of the products produced, in this case the CO_2. But don't forget that the main **function** of the process is to manufacture......what? _____

Your lab instructor will explain how to measure the CO_2. In general, it will be measured by volume displacement of water by CO_2. Remember, the more CO_2 produced, the faster fermentation is occurring, and the more ATP and alcohol are produced.

Next lab period, you will perform additional experiments detailing how variables like temperature, sugar, or other factors affect the rate of the process. The week after that, you will present and discuss your results. Your lab instructor will provide additional information.

PROCEDURES

1. Work with others at your table.
2. First, verify the cellular attributes of yeast by examining a drop of the yeast solution under the microscope. Use a slide, a drop of yeast culture, and a plastic cover slip. Refer back to Appendix 5 and your instructor for additional information regarding use of a microscope. Be sure to clean and dry the slide when finished, and return it to the box. You may discard the cover slip.
3. You will next need to mix up your "mash" for fermentation by adding 175 ml of naturally sweetened grape juice to a flask.
4. Next, find the yeast mixture, **shake it up**, and then add 40 ml of the yeast solution to the same flask.
5. Cover the mouth of the flask with a piece of plastic wrap and shake the flask.
6. Everything is at room temperature, but measure and <u>record the temperature</u> of the final mash in degrees Celsius: _____.
7. Now **tightly** attach a rubber stopper with a flexible tube to the top of the flask and insert the end of the rubber tube into a 50ml graduated cylinder filled with water and inverted into a bowl of water (see Figure 5.1). Note that the bowl must be about half filled with water. Before inverting the graduated cylinder, fill it completely with water, cover the opening of the cylinder with your hand or thumb, and then invert the cylinder into the water bowl making sure that the mouth of the cylinder is below water level. Then, release your hand or thumb. The water will stay in the cylinder. If it does not, then try again.
8. Note the **exact** position of the water level in the graduated cylinder. This is your starting point at time zero.
9. Now you can insert the rubber tubing underneath the mouth of the graduated cylinder and begin collecting CO_2.
10. Gently swirl the flask with the yeast just prior to making a measurement to keep the contents mixed and to help release the gas. Swirl the same way each time. Do not swirl or shake so violently that fluids are forced up into the tube; this could invalidate results.
11. Note the volume of gas produced (in mls) every 5 minutes for 35 minutes (your instructor may choose a different time span). Record this information in Table 5.1. Your instructor may ask you to put this data on the board or in a spreadsheet.

12. If, during the experiment, the gas produced causes all the water in the inverted cylinder to be pushed out, then quickly refill the cylinder with water and continue.

13. Plot the data you (and/or the class) collected using the space in Figure 5.2.

14. **Be sure** to clean all glassware thoroughly with detergent when finished.

Figure 5.1. Fermentation measurement equipment set-up, used to collect and measure carbon dioxide production in milliliters (ml).

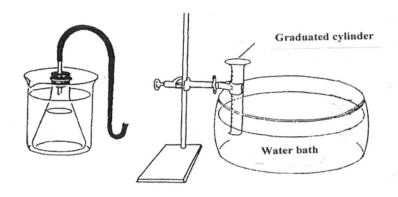

Table 5.1. Total cumulative CO_2 production in milliliters (ml) at five minute intervals.

Time (min)	5	10	15	20	25	30	35	
Ml CO_2								

QUESTIONS:

1. How many milliliters (ml) of CO_2 were produced during the 35 minute period for your group?   For the class?

2. What products of fermentation are in the flask that this process did <u>not</u> measure?

3. What is the <u>function</u> of fermentation for yeast cells?

4. Why do you suppose that the alcoholic content of wine is always about 10–12%? Think about what increasing alcohol concentrations might do to the living yeast cells.

Figure 5.2. Milliliters of CO_2 produced at 5 minute intervals over 35 minutes.

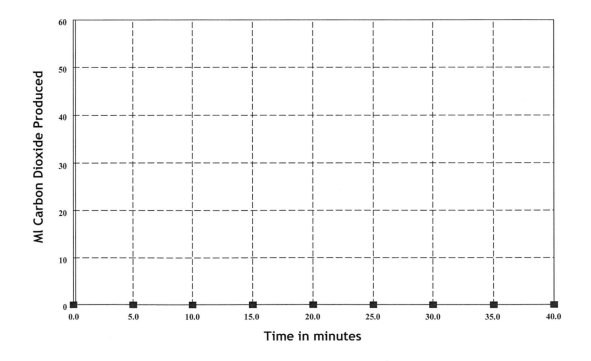

III. PLANNING THE NEXT LAB SESSION

Next session's activities must be planned. It is your job to construct and then test hypotheses regarding the effects of variables of your choice on the rate of fermentation as measured by CO_2 production. Only through experimentation such as this could people learn how to precisely control this economically important process.

5.3 Sugar Types—the Substrates

Substrates are reactant molecules which, in fermentation, are broken apart into simpler compounds as the process proceeds. Yeast cells require substrates as an energy source if they are to accomplish fermentation which functions to make ATPs for themselves as well as to produce alcohol and CO_2 wastes which we can measure.

The substrates available in lab are as follows:

1. **Glucose**. This is a monosaccharide carbohydrate (a simple sugar) and can be used directly by all cells as an energy source to manufacture ATPs. Glucose is first converted to pyruvate molecules during glycolysis before entering the fermentation process in yeast cells.

2. **Sucrose**. This is a disaccharide carbohydrate or a double sugar and is the most common sweetener. This double sugar requires the use of one glucose molecule and one fructose molecule (each are monosaccharides) to construct each sucrose molecule. When we or yeast cells consume sucrose, enzymes must break apart the disaccharide molecule into glucose and fructose before the cells can utilize them to make ATP molecules.

3. **Mannitol**. This is a sugar alcohol. It has about half the calories of sugar and is half as sweet. It has trouble diffusing into the body and so does well as an artificial sweetener, if used in moderation. Why in moderation? That is because its use can lead to mild intestinal upset and diarrhea. It is often used to lightly coat the surface of chewing gum, giving the gum both an initial sweet taste and a slight cooling effect since it also has a "negative heat of solution."

Design your experiments NOW **as a group** and be prepared to start them next lab session. Remember to use replicates and controls. You will also be expected to graph out and analyze your data and determine whether or not to accept your hypothesis. Remember, you can only use variables available in the lab. **Variables you can consider** are temperature, yeast concentration, sugar concentration, and sugar type (glucose, sucrose, and mannitol). Text box 5.3 provides additional information about these substrates. We will <u>also have</u>

Splenda, an artificial sweetener (see the Appendix at the end of this lab for more information about Splenda). If you are not sure what these various substances are and want to use them, look them up on line or in an organic chemistry text to obtain more information. The substrates will be in granulated form and not in solution.

SPECIAL CAUTIONS OR INSTRUCTIONS:

1. Please note that if you are NOT using sugar as a variable, then you MUST use the sweetened grape juice in your preparations. If sugar amounts are to be the variable, then use the unsweetened juice.

2. Do not add so much fluid to the flask that the glass tubing extending from the bottom of the stopper is immersed in the fluid. There MUST be an air space in between the fluid in the flask and the glass tubing or else the emerging CO_2 will not be measurable.

3. You probably will only be able to do one replicate of your experiment. Due to time factors, **be sure** to set up and do both experimental runs at the same time.

For purposes of planning, you should know that one teaspoon of sugar weighs about 4 grams. One teaspoon of Splenda, an artificial sweetener, weighs about 0.73 grams. When using Splenda in food, you substitute it for sugar based on its volume (1 tsp sugar = 1 tsp Splenda). You will need to measure your substrates using an electronic balance which registers in grams, not a volumetric measure. So, do not report your measurements in teaspoons. The teaspoon information was given to provide perspective.

Remember, knowing something about the substances you use will help you to understand your results and will produce a better Discussion section in the report you may be required to write.

BE SURE to determine the following before you leave lab today:

MY HYPOTHESIS

MY EXPERIMENTAL PROTOCOL

Also be sure to check with your instructor about your plans before leaving the laboratory. Text box 5.4 outlines the methods you could use to test the effects of varying temperature on fermentation in yeast.

5.4 Maintaining the yeast at different temperatures:

Note that the flask in Figure 5.1 is placed in a beaker of water. By using combinations of hot and cold tap water, ice and a hot plate you can adjust the temperature of the water in the beaker. But **you must continue to monitor and adjust** the water in those beakers throughout your experiment so that the temperature(s) you have chosen stays relatively stable. So, you must insert a thermometer into the beakers along with the flask to monitor temperatures.

After the water temperature is adjusted, add the flask with the yeast and other contents. <u>But do not yet insert the rubber tubing into the graduated cylinder</u>. First, let the contents of the flask sit at the chosen temperature for 10 minutes. This allows the contents of the flask to **equilibrate** (i.e. reach the same temperature as the water in the beaker). After the contents of the flask equilibrate, you can then insert the rubber tubing into the mouth of the graduated cylinder and begin your measurements. Try to explain the results based upon optimum temperatures for the enzymes responsible for controlling the process. Check a source for more information about this.

IV. DATA ANALYSES AND REPORTS

After collecting your data, you must be able to present it in tables and figures in such a way that others can understand what it was that you did. Remember, using and graphing <u>mean</u> values is often a good way to express data. The use of descriptive statistics is also encouraged. Read Appendix 4, Data Analyses, for appropriate methods and techniques.

The **third week** of this project will require your group to present and discuss their data. You may also be required to turn in a lab report. If so, each person in your group is responsible for writing their own report. These reports are to be written independently. The only similarity within your group should be the data. Your instructor will tell you his or her particular expectations.

Appendix 2 outlines expectations for both written and oral lab reports while Appendix 3 outlines expectations for references. Your instructor may modify these guidelines.

APPENDIX—SPLENDA FACTS

The author of this book sent the following inquiry to Splenda:

-----Original Message-----
Sent: 04/17/2007 15:47:51
Subject: Question/Comment

Consumer stated: I noticed that the label for Splenda no calorie sweetener says that Splenda has small amounts of calories and carbohydrates. What is the specific form of carbohydrate that is in this product, and how many calories and grams of carbohydrate are actually in a serving (= 1 teaspoon)?

Dear Ron,

Thank you for taking the time to contact us regarding SPLENDA* Brand products.

Maltodextrin is a carbohydrate derived from corn starch which is added to SPLENDA* Granular to make it more convenient to use in a home kitchen environment. It contributes 1/2 gram of carbohydrate or the equivalent of 2 calories per teaspoon. Up to 6 teaspoons of SPLENDA* Granular are considered a "free" food in a sugar-restricted diet. When used in larger amounts, as in cooking or baking, these calories should be accounted for in the daily allowances towards the bread/starch exchange. As an example, 5/8 cup of SPLENDA* Granular contributes 15 g carbohydrate and is counted as 1 starch food choice.

Adding dextrose to our SPLENDA* packets results in a more appetizing product that doesn't fizz or float on your drink. Dextrose can be sourced from many plants but the dextrose in our product is most likely from corn. Dextrose and maltodextrin contribute a total of 1 gram of carbohydrate or 4 calories per packet. Therefore, three SPLENDA* Packets may be considered a "free" food, however, when used in greater quantities, the calories from SPLENDA* Packets should be counted towards the fruit exchange.

Should you require further information, please e-mail us aqain or call the Information Centre at: 1 800 561-0070.

Sincerely,

Tanya
*Trademark
www.splenda.ca

To learn more about Splenda (sucralose is its technical name) visit the Splenda web site:

http://tinyurl.com/6uh6z8t

Then, click on "What is in SPLENDA sweetener products" or other FAQS that may interest you.

Finally, just for fun, here is a link to a song that covers alcoholic fermentation as well as the effects that alcohol has on the body from a biological perspective:

http://tinyurl.com/8294jtb

LAB 6. ECOLOGY: NUTRIENT POLLUTION

Ecology is a word that is often used quite carelessly. "Save the ecology"; "It's hurting the ecology." But in the biological sciences, this word has a specific meaning. Ecology is the study of the interactions of living organisms in nature both within and between different species and the nonliving environment. Potentially, just about everything that affects organisms could be included into an ecological study.

Ecology means much more than nature studies and environmental biology. Ecologists study how nature works from the deep seas to the tops of mountains. They study the creatures from all the kingdoms, both microscopic and macroscopic. Many ecologists are interested in the factors that limit distribution and abundance of species. Populations, including human populations, have the capacity to grow exponentially. Their growth is only limited by their required resources such as nutrients, water and space, and by the actions of other organisms such as predators, competitors, parasites, and in some cases, human activities. But for a while, until those factors kick in, population growth over time can be huge. For example, the human population first reached 1 billion in 1850, 2 billion in 1930, 4 billion in 1970, and in 2015 human populations reached 7.32 billion. By 2050 we may reach 9–11 billion people! This will put even more pressure on the environment. There are factors that affect such growth rates. Both **abiotic** (non-living) factors like changing weather patterns, soil nutrients, and pollution, and **biotic** factors like competition and predation eventually will slow, stop, or reverse such trends in the natural world.

Like most types of biological studies, ecological studies typically include the construction and testing of hypotheses. For example, an ecologist might test the hypothesis that "...decreasing ground water levels accelerate the destruction of forests..." Another example might be "...wolf predation pressure will increase the diversity of prey animals in the forest..." A third example could be "...nitrogen and phosphorus run off from the land into the Chesapeake Bay affects algae populations which in turn reduces animal populations..."   (How would one go about testing these hypotheses?). The result of such studies will be data that must be analyzed and used to address the hypotheses. We use such techniques to learn how nature functions. This enables scientists to formulate opinions as to the effect of human activities on natural systems.

ECOBEAKER™: NUTRIENT POLLUTION

Introduction

Energy, Nutrients, and Trophic Relationships

The dynamics of all ecosystems revolve around two key processes: energy flow and nutrient cycling. Most energy flow starts with the sun. **Autotrophs** (*autos* = self + *trophe* = food), such as plants, use solar energy to generate organic tissue from inorganic chemicals. Autotrophic organisms are considered to be **primary producers**, because they produce the organic molecules that fuel other organisms. **Heterotrophs** (*heteros* = another + *trophe* = food) obtain energy for growth and maintenance from the organisms they consume. Organisms that eat primary producers (e.g., herbivores) are known as **primary consumers**. Predators of herbivores are considered **secondary consumers**, and predators of predators are **tertiary consumers**. At each of these trophic levels, some of the solar energy initially converted into chemical energy by autotrophs is passed along, but some is dissipated as heat.

Organic molecules not only store the energy that powers living organisms but are the building blocks with which organisms are constructed. Cells and tissues are made from a diversity of organic molecules like amino acids to make proteins and nucleic acids to form DNA. These specialized molecules require a variety of chemical elements including carbon, hydrogen, oxygen, nitrogen, phosphorus and sulfur, as well as small amounts of elements like potassium and sodium. These required elements are called **nutrients**. The nutrients in an ecosystem come from the air, water, soil, and rocks. In many environments, one or more of the nutrients required by the local primary producers is in short supply, and the lack of such a **limiting nutrient** can limit growth of living things in the area (i.e., if you add that nutrient, growth increases). Many aquatic systems are nutrient limited, usually by phosphorus (P) or nitrogen (N). The natural input of these elements to a body of water, such as a lake can be a slow process. For example, most P in streams and lakes comes from the weathering of rocks. In places where the rocks contain little P or weather slowly, there may be very little P in the water. For this reason, many bodies of water could support far more life if only they had a bit of fertilizer.

Inadvertently (and occasionally on purpose), humans supply this fertilizer. Every time you flush your toilet, its contents go somewhere, and quite often that somewhere is a nearby body of water. Mixed in with your feces are food scraps from your kitchen sink, along with the soap you used to wash your dishes and clothes (which may contain phosphates). Also mixed in is extra fertilizer from people's lawns, ammonia (NH_3--which contains nitrogen) from industrial facilities, and all the other odds and ends that find their way into city pipes and storm drains. Wherever this mixture of pollutants ends up receives a large input of nutrients. If the pollution ends up in water, those nutrients usually drive growth of the local primary producers, the **phytoplankton** (algae and cyanobacteria).

Too Much of a Good Thing? Nutrients and Algal Blooms

If you've ever lived near a lake experiencing an algal bloom, you know it is not pleasant. Good lake water, in most people's opinion, is not green and smelly. It is odorless and clear, which generally means it is nutrient-poor, which limits the growth of phytoplankton. When phytoplankton die, they sink to the bottom of the lake and undergo decomposition, a process which uses oxygen in much the same way you use oxygen when you breathe. When phytoplankton populations are large, the resulting high rate of decomposition can strip the oxygen from the water and turn a lake **anoxic** (i.e., lacking oxygen). Many animals cannot survive if oxygen levels drop too low, generally below about 2 mg/liter. Furthermore, if certain types of cyanobacteria are present, algal blooms can result in increased toxin levels in the water, which can cause human health problems. For all of these reasons, people do not usually like lakes that are overly nutrient-rich.

Here's where you come into the picture. When you initiate the Nutrient Pollution laboratory you will be (virtually) transported back in time to the early 1950s, when many cities were experiencing a post-war population boom. With larger populations came increased sewage and much of the sewage was disposed of in the nearest body of water. A few years prior to your arrival, your city built a sewage system that empties into a lake near your home. You estimate that they will soon be tripling the lake's nutrient input rate. You've started to see changes in the species dominating the lake, and you are worried about this turn of events. Being a concerned citizen, you decide to do some experiments with the goal of trying to predict what's going to happen to your lake if the city keeps dumping raw sewage into it. The nutrient that most often limits growth in lakes is phosphorus, so in your experiments, you'll concentrate on phosphorus. You are also concerned, because you know sewage often contains toxins such as heavy metals that affect animals much more than plants. You want to know if the added toxins might have additional effects on the lake.

You have access to a research station with a set of small lakes just outside of town for your experiments. Using these lakes, you will conduct experiments to determine the effects of adding phosphorus and toxins. You will then use your results to write a letter to the editor of your local paper. Your goal is to tell the public what's likely to happen if they keep increasing the sewage dumped into the lake.

The Lake Model in SimBio Virtual Labs

This lab uses a lake simulation to explore how the addition of nutrients (and toxins) can influence a lake's community and potentially lead to algal blooms. The virtual lake includes five simulated species each which has a specific role in the community (see table next page).

The two types of phytoplankton in the lake model are green algae and cyanobacteria (sometimes referred to as blue-green algae). Green algae are a diverse group, but the model treats them as one species. Cyanobacteria are photosynthetic bacteria. Many cyanobacteria, including the ones in this model, are also capable of nitrogen fixation. The phytoplankton and zooplankton both have stages in their life cycles in which they go dormant. This means that even if they disappear from the water in the lake, some dormant individuals in the mud at the bottom will eventually emerge and repopulate the lake. The model also includes detritivores that decompose the dead bodies of the organisms in the lake. Lake detritivores are microscopic and not shown in the simulation, but you will know they are there because decomposition uses oxygen, and the dissolved oxygen (DO) level is constantly monitored with a probe at the bottom of the lake.

SPECIES	TYPE OF ORGANISM
1. Green Algae	Phytoplankton (primary producer)
2. Cyanobacteria	Phytoplankton (primary producer)
3. *Bosmina*	Zooplankton (primary consumer)
4. *Daphnia*	Zooplankton (primary consumer)
5. Trout	Fish (secondary consumer)

A few other details about the lake model are important to know about. **Phosphorus** and **nitrogen** are two **nutrients** that commonly limit growth in lakes, so the simulated lake "budget" is primarily based on these two nutrients. Phytoplankton growth not only depends on phosphorus and nitrogen concentrations but also on the amount of light energy available. Light is limited by lake depth and by phytoplankton, which block light when populations are large. The consumers in the lake also need phosphorus and nitrogen to grow, which they get from their prey. Each time a zooplankton or trout encounters a prey item, it has a certain chance of catching it. A certain percentage of the nutrients in the captured prey are taken up, and the rest are excreted back into the lake water. In addition, small amounts of nitrogen and phosphorus are constantly being added to the lake from outside, and a percentage of what's currently in the lake is constantly being lost through the lake's outlet. Finally, you might notice that phytoplankton have different movement patterns at different depths of the lake.

Some Important Terms and Concepts

Ecosystem Ecology

Ecosystems include both the biological and physical components of a community. Ecosystem ecologists study the flow of energy and the cycling of materials through ecosystems.

Eutrophication

Lakes and other bodies of water that have particularly large populations of primary producers are considered to be eutrophic. Eutrophication, or increased primary productivity, occurs when extra nutrients are added to a lake. When eutrophication occurs naturally (e.g., as lakes age), it is typically a gradual process. However, eutrophication can also occur rapidly when people dump fertilizer or sewage into lakes. If nutrient levels become high enough, lake communities can literally be suffocated by huge blooms of phytoplankton. These blooms pose a particular threat to the environment if the phytoplankton includes toxin-producing species.

Biological Magnification

Organisms can inadvertently consume toxins by drinking polluted water or eating other organisms that contain toxins. Some of these substances can be metabolized and excreted, but others accumulate in the body. If primary consumers eat primary producers that contain toxins, the toxins will be transferred to the consumers. If the toxins are not excreted, they will accumulate as more and more toxic prey are consumed. Similarly, the toxins that have accumulated in the primary consumers will be passed on to their predators, the secondary consumers. In this manner, accumulating toxins concentrate as they move up the food chain through successive trophic levels. This process of increasing toxin concentration through successive links in a food chain is referred to as biological magnification.

EXERCISE 1. STARTING UP

[1]   Before you start playing with the simulation model, you should read the introductory material. The background information will help you understand the simulation model and answer questions correctly.

[2]   Start the program by double-clicking the **SIMBIO VIRTUAL LABS** icon on your computer or by selecting it from the Start Menu on your computer.

[3]   When **SIMBIO VIRTUAL LABS** opens, select **NUTRIENT POLLUTION** from the **EcoBeaker** suite.

You will see a number of different panels on the screen:

- The upper left panel shows a (virtual) lake in the early 1950s that is not yet heavily impacted by people and their pollution; this is where you will begin your investigations by learning a bit about the species in the lake.

- Bar graphs on the right will show the population sizes of all the organisms in the lake.

- A legend above the graphs shows the species in the lake and their icons.

- You will run the simulation using the Control Panel in the bottom left corner on the screen. To the right of the Control Panel is a set of Tools that you will use for doing your experiments. These will be described as you need them.

[4]   Click on the names in the **Species Legend** in the upper right corner of the screen to bring up library pages for each group of species. Use the library to complete the following questions:

[Q1]   **Which species in the simulation is capable of nitrogen fixation?**

[Q2]   **Members of which species in the simulation are commonly known as "water fleas?"**

[5]   Start the simulation by clicking the **GO** button in the **Control Panel** and watch the action for a bit.

[Q3]   **Briefly describe what happens in the simulation when phytoplankton dies.** (Hint: They change color.)

[6]   Click the **STOP** button to pause the simulation.

[7]   Click the **MICROSCOPE** ("View organism") tool button at the bottom of the

screen to activate your mobile "Gut-o-Scope" (patent pending). Then click on individuals in the lake to see what they last consumed. (NOTE: this only works for organisms with guts!)

[Q4]   Based on your sampling, what do *Bosmina* in the lake eat?

[Q5]   Based on your sampling, what do *Daphnia* in the lake eat?

[Q6]   Based on your sampling, what do Trout in the lake eat?

[8]   When there are not very many individuals of a particular species present, just by chance it is less likely that they will show up in gut content samples. In this lake, *Bosmina* only eat green algae whereas *Daphnia* eat both green algae and cyanobacteria. Trout eat BOTH of the primary consumers.

[Q7]   After reading the above statement, did you miss any species in your gut content sampling? If so, which ones?

EXERCISE 2: P IN THE WATER

A research station has a set of small experimental lakes you can alter as you need, and a research boat that is outfitted with monitoring equipment. As you recall from reading the Introduction, you are concerned about the risk of algal blooms that might occur with increased phosphorus added to the lake as the town grows. Because green algae tend to outcompete cyanobacteria, algal blooms are usually dominated by green algae. Therefore, your first set of experiments focuses on what happens to green algae when phosphorus (P) is increased. While you're at it, you will record oxygen levels at the bottom of the lake to see any links between anoxia (lack of oxygen) and water pollution.

[1] Select **P IN THE WATER** from the **SELECT AN EXERCISE** menu at the top of the screen.

[2] Click **PHOSPHORUS** in the **Chemical Input** options (to the right of the **Tools**). Make sure it is set to 1x (i.e., no extra phosphorus).

[3] Click the **STEP 52 WEEKS** button to run the simulation for one year. (Note: You can adjust the speed of the simulation with the **SPEED SLIDER** tool in the **Control Panel** next to the **RESET** button.)

[3.1] **When the simulation stops, record the population size of green algae (from the graph), and the dissolved oxygen (DO) level** (which you can read either from the graph or from the meter at the bottom of the lake) **in the first row of the following data table.**

HELPFUL HINT: if you click on the colored bars in the Population Size graph, the numbers (population sizes) that the bars represent will pop up!

4] Click the **RESET** button to start again with a new experimental lake.

[5] Increase **PHOSPHORUS** to 2x (double the starting concentration). Then click the **STEP 52 WEEKS** button to run the simulation for one year.

[5.1] **Record your data in the second row of the following data table.**

[6] Click the **RESET** button, then increase **PHOSPHORUS** to 3x (triple the starting concentration). Then click the **STEP 52 WEEKS** button.

[6.1]   Record your data in the third row of the data table below.

Data Table for Phosphorus Input Experiment

PHOSPHORUS INPUT	GREEN ALGAE POPULATION SIZE	DISSOLVED OXYGEN (mg/L)
1X		
2X		
3X		

[6.2]   Draw a line graph of your green algae population size data to show how green algae relate to phosphorus input levels. Don't worry about being too precise; you can graph approximate values.

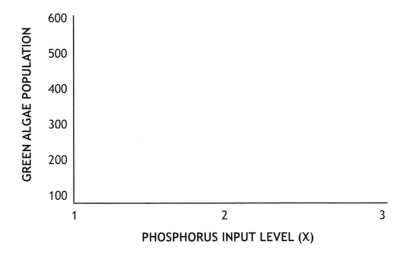

[Q8]   Does the relationship between green algae population size and phosphorus level indicate that phosphorus was a limiting nutrient for green algae in the lake? Explain.

[6.4] You also have recorded data from the oxygen meter at the bottom of the lake. Now draw a line graph showing how oxygen relates to phytoplankton population size. Again, don't worry about being too precise; you can use approximate values of your data.

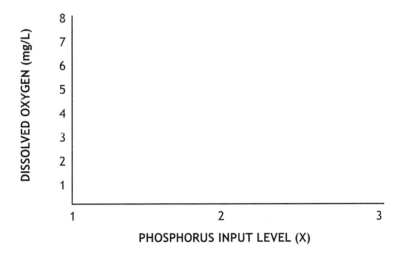

[Q9] What is the relationship between dissolved oxygen and phosphorus in the lake?

[Q10] Based on your two graphs, what is the relationship between green algae population size and dissolved oxygen the lake? Provide a biological explanation for your answer.

EXERCISE 3: DO OR DIE

When you added phosphorus to your experimental lake in the previous exercise, the green algae population increased and the dissolved oxygen (= DO) decreased. But what would happen in a more realistic lake with more species? You will now repeat the phosphorus addition experiment in a lake that is identical to the one in the previous experiment, except that it also includes zooplankton and trout.

[1] Select **DO OR DIE** from the **SELECT AN EXERCISE** menu at the top of the screen. The lake will now include green algae, cyanobacteria, *Daphnia, Bosmina,*

88

and trout. If you look at the following data table, you will see that you will be collecting the same data as before. Before you start these experiments, first make some predictions.

[Q11]   Consider the trophic relationships of the species. Do you think the green algae populations will be smaller, larger, or about the same as in your previous experiments? Explain your reasoning.

[Q12]   Do you think the dissolved oxygen concentration will be lower, higher, or about the same as in the previous experiment? Explain your reasoning.

[Q13]   Which species do you expect to be impacted the most by increased phosphorus, and why?

[2]   Make sure the **PHOSPHORUS** level is set at 1x and, as before, click the **STEP 52 WEEKS** button to run the simulation for one year.

[2.1]   When the simulation stops, record the population sizes of green algae and the concentration of dissolved oxygen (DO) in the first row of the data table that follows.

Data Table for Phosphorus Input Experiment

Phosphorus Input	Green Algae Population Size	Dissolved Oxygen (mg/l)
1X		
2X		
3X		

[3] Compare your new data to the corresponding data in the first row in the date table from Exercise 2.

[Q14] Were your predictions correct? How different are the phytoplankton population sizes and dissolved oxygen levels from the previous experiment?

[4] RESET the simulation, increase PHOSPHORUS to 2x and click the STEP 52 WEEKS button to run the simulation for one year.

[4.1] Record your data in the second row of the data table above.

[5] RESET the simulation, increase PHOSPHORUS to 3x and click the STEP 52 WEEKS button to run the simulation for one year.

[5.1] Record your data in the third row of the data table above. (Do not RESET the simulation.)

90

[6]   You should have found that the dissolved oxygen concentrations in this set of experiments were consistently higher than in the lake without zooplankton and trout even though the lakes and phosphorus inputs were identical. (Since there's some random variability in the underlying model, there's a small chance your data did not show this, but typically this is the pattern that emerges.)

[Q15]   **Why could having consumers as well as producers present change the amount of dissolved oxygen in the lake?**

[7]   You may have noticed that the population sizes bounced around more with additional species present. This is due to interactions between trophic levels. For example, when trout eat zooplankton, there are fewer zooplankton around to eat the phytoplankton so the phytoplankton population sizes increases. The additional phytoplankton support more zooplankton, so the zooplankton population increases, which in turn supports additional trout, and so on. The system is much more dynamic than before.

[8]   Because the system is so dynamic, it can take longer for patterns to emerge. You know that a dissolved oxygen level below 2.0 is considered to be dangerously low. To see if the dissolved oxygen level at the highest phosphorus addition level might go below 2.0 over time, run the simulation by clicking the **GO** button and observe what happens.

[Q16]   **Does the dissolved oxygen continue to drop over time?**

[Q17]   **What would happen if the dissolved oxygen drops below 2.0? (You might have to be patient and let the simulation run a bit...)**

EXERCISE 4. TOXINS

Sewage can contain dangerous toxins. It is known that mercury in lakes can be a major health hazard; toxic effects of mercury poisoning include damage to the brain, kidneys, and lungs. It is also known that many heavy metals are prone to biological magnification (a process described in the Introduction.) You don't know whether your city's sewage will be toxic, but in case it is, you write a grant proposal to study the effects of adding the heavy metal mercury[1] to your experimental lake. Your grant is funded, complete with money for assistants to do the tedious sampling of toxin levels in the body tissues of organisms. You just need to visit the experimental lake once a year for four years to collect and analyze the summarized data.

[1]   One objective of your experiment is to determine whether mercury biomagnifies.

   [Q18]   If mercury biomagnifies, in which of the below organisms would you expect to find the highest mercury levels in a lake with mercury contamination? (Circle one)

   Algae   Zooplankton   Trout

   [Q19]   Briefly explain your selection.

[2]   Select **TOXINS** from the **SELECT AN EXERCISE** menu at the top of the screen. Before you start the experiment (which causes mercury to be added to the lake), click the **SAMPLE TOXINS** button (the little meter to the right of the microscope). This will pop up a window showing the current average mercury level in each species in the lake water.

---

[1] Mercury is found in different forms in the environment. The most important form for cities concerned about their water resources to track is compound called methyl mercury. For simplicity, throughout this lab, we refer to methyl mercury simply as mercury.

[2.1] Copy the Time = 0 data for mercury levels in the organisms on the following data table. (The mercury has not yet been added to the lake, so you should be recording a lot of zeros.)

TOXIN ANALYSIS DATA: Time = 0

	POPULATION SIZE	MERCURY
Green Algae		ng/g
Cyanobacteria		ng/g
Daphnia		ng/g
Bosmina		ng/g
Trout		ng/g

[3] Use the STEP 52 button to run the simulation for one year.

[3.1] Record your data below. Then repeat two more times (i.e., run for 3 years total) and record your data in the space provided on the corresponding data tables on the next page. (Since you are tracking what happens over time, do *not* hit the RESET button between runs!!)

TOXIN ANALYSIS DATA: Time = 1 year (52 weeks)

	POPULATION SIZE	MERCURY
Green Algae		ng/g
Cyanobacteria		ng/g
Daphnia		ng/g
Bosmina		ng/g
Trout		ng/g

TOXIN ANALYSIS DATA: Time = 2 years (104 weeks)

	POPULATION SIZE	MERCURY
Green Algae		ng/g
Cyanobacteria		ng/g
Daphnia		ng/g
Bosmina		ng/g
Trout		ng/g

TOXIN ANALYSIS DATA: Time = 3 years (156 weeks)

	POPULATION SIZE	MERCURY
Green Algae		ng/g
Cyanobacteria		ng/g
Daphnia		ng/g
Bosmina		ng/g
Trout		ng/g

[3.2] Create a line graph showing mercury concentration over a three-year interval in each species. Your graph will include 5 lines, one for each species; be sure to label which line is for which species. Don't worry about being precise; you can graph approximate values!

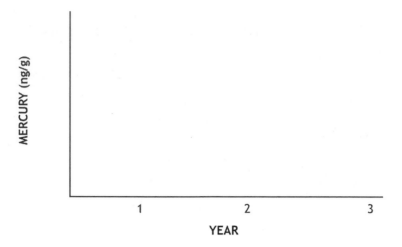

[Q20]   Is there more mercury in the phytoplankton at the base of the food chain or in the fish at the top? Does this change over time?

[Q21]   Does your graph show evidence for biomagnification of mercury in this lake? Explain.

EXERCISE 5. MYSTERY IN THE LAKE

Not only have you become an expert on nutrient pollution in lakes, you have also learned how to travel through time! You have transported yourself from the lake where you started in the 1950s to the same lake today. It's a mess! Lots of sewage is being dumped in the lake, and there is also a problem with runoff (contaminated water flowing into the lake) from nearby industry. The lake is experiencing a toxic algal bloom because the cyanobacteria in the lake are producing a chemical called **microcystin**, a liver toxin that can make people sick when they drink the water. It is unusual to find more cyanobacteria in a lake than green algae, as typically green algae are superior competitors. Your challenge is to figure out what is happening in the lake, and in particular, why there are more cyanobacteria than green algae.

[1] Select **MYSTERY LAKE** from the **SELECT AN EXERCISE** menu at the top of the screen. In this more open-ended exercise, you have access to all of the tools and can design your own experiments. You can adjust the **CHEMICAL INPUTS** for both phosphorus and nitrogen, and can now even remove nutrients (i.e., by setting the **CHEMICAL INPUTS** to zero).

[2] In most lakes, green algae are at a competitive advantage over cyanobactera, but in this lake the cyanobacteria dominate. There is something about the chemistry of this lake that allows this to happen.

[Q22] Is there a difference in the biology of these two types of organisms that might lead to hypotheses for what is happening in this lake? Look back at the natural history as needed and then state your hypotheses and explain your reasoning.

[Q23] If a nutrient is limited for a particular species, what happens when you add more of that nutrient to the system?

[Q24] If a nutrient is NOT limited for a particular species, what happens when you add more of that nutrient to the system?

[3] Experiment with chemical inputs to see if you can find evidence to support your hypotheses above for why cyanobacteria may be outcompeting green algae in this lake.

[Q25] Describe your experiments and the results that support your answer. Feel free to describe any other interesting findings as well!

EXERCISE 6: LETTER TO THE EDITOR AND/OR ANNOTATED BIBLIOGRAPHY

1. You may be required to write a letter to the editor of your local newspaper expressing your informed opinion about your city's plan to dump sewage into the lake near your house. **Be sure to support your opinion with some of the data you collected and the facts and ideas you learned. You may need to attach additional sheets.** Your instructor will specify your responsibilities here which may include the use of reference material.

2. In lieu of this exercise, or, in addition to this exercise, your instructor may direct you to run additional simulations that you construct.

3. You may also be required to construct an **annotated bibliography** using one or two primary journal articles whose contents relate directly to this lab exercise. See Appendix B for more information.

> An annotated bibliography is a list of (in this case) article citations followed by a brief (about 100 words) description of the article including any evaluative comments.

The National Oceanic and Atmospheric Administration (NOAA) website (1) and the Environmental Protection Agency's (EPA) website (2) will provide additional information:

1. **http://tinyurl.com/puhlaxn**

2. **http://tinyurl.com/omfq7dj**

Appendix A-- Nutrient Enrichment

Sewage is not a new problem. Two thousand years ago, the Romans were building sewage systems, and every town and city before and since have had to deal somehow with what to do with the waste products of its inhabitants (even if the "solution" was just to leave it in the street until rain washed it away). In the late 1800s and early 1900s, scientists in Europe and North America started studying the effects of sewage in water, similar to what you did in this lab.

One of the most famous of these studies happened in Lake Washington, an 18-mile-long lake that forms one border for the city of Seattle, in the northwestern U.S. By the middle of the century, there was an abundance of data on what happened to lakes when nutrients, especially phosphorus, were added to them. Dr. Tommy Edmondson, a limnologist at the University of Washington, along with many of his students, surveyed Lake Washington in 1950 and again in 1955. Although these surveys were not specifically looking for effects of sewage on the lake's water quality, in 1955 they noticed some of the warning signs for a lake about to go bad—rising phosphorus levels and rising levels of certain algal species. Edmondson raised a warning cry in Seattle and helped spearhead a campaign to move the city's sewage outflow from Lake Washington to the ocean, where it would do less damage. The lake responded faster than anyone expected. While new sewage lines were being built, sewage continued going into the lake, and the lake began experiencing algal blooms and foul-smelling water. Within three years of completion of the sewage diversion, the water quality was better than it had been even in 1950 when Edmondson first sampled. Similar improvements have now been seen in other lakes around the world after nearby communities changed how sewage and other nutrient sources were processed.

Although most point sources of water pollution (like sewage and industrial by-products) are now fairly well-regulated, non-point sources, such as agricultural run-off and detritus washed down city storm drains, are still a big problem. Most bodies of water that are near human establishments are becoming more and more eutrophic (nutrient rich), and we can anticipate increasing problems with algal blooms, fish poisoning, and other water quality issues in the future. Not only are freshwater lakes and rivers affected, but so are the coasts of our oceans. Red and brown tides, for instance, have been linked to increases in nutrients in coastal waters. Fortunately, among the array of environmental problems currently facing the world, this is one of the most easily solved. Simple things like reducing the amount of fertilizer used on fields (which often is more than the crops can use anyway), reducing the amount of waste products each household disposes of, putting swamps or other natural buffer zones between people and waterways, and making better sewage systems can all substantially reduce the amount of nutrients that get into the water. Hopefully, as was the case with Lake Washington, we'll start working on the solutions before the problems get too out of hand.

REFERENCES

Edmondson, W. T. 1991. The Uses of Ecology: Lake Washington and Beyond. University of Washington Press, Seattle, WA.

Carpenter, S.R., N.F. Caraco, D.L. Correll, R.W. Howarth, A.N. Sharpley, V.H. Smith. 1998. Nonpoint pollution of surface waters with phosphorus and nitrogen. *Issues in Ecology* 3: 1–12.

Swackhamer, D.L., H.W. Paerl, S.J. Eisenreich, J. Hurley, K.C. Hornbuckle, M. McLachlan, D. Mount, D. Muir, and D. Schindler. 2004. Impacts of atmospheric pollutants on aquatic ecosystems. *Issues in Ecology* 12: 1–24.

Vitousek, P.M., H.A. Mooney, J. Lubchenco, J.M. Melillo. 1997. Human domination of Earth's ecosystems. *Science* 277: 494–499.

Appendix B—Writing an Annotated Bibliography

THE PROCESS

Creating an annotated bibliography calls for the application of a variety of intellectual skills: concise exposition, succinct analysis, and informed library research.

First, **locate** and record citations to the primary journal articles or periodicals, that may contain useful information and ideas about your topic. Appendix 3 at the back of this book provides information that will help you find appropriate articles. Briefly examine and review the actual items. Then choose those works that provide a variety of perspectives on your topic.

Cite the article, or document using the appropriate style. The reference list at the top of this page is written using the correct style. For journal articles, like the three at the top of this page, note that first is the author (last name first), then the year of publication, then the title of the article, followed by the volume number and the page number of the first and last pages in the article. Refer back to these articles as models including what type of punctuation to use and where the proper punctuation goes.

Writing the annotation. Each citation will be followed by an annotation, which is a descriptive and evaluative paragraph. In your annotation, be sure to 1) clearly state the **purpose** of the article, 2) explain the major **results**, and 3) critically **evaluate** the article.

What follows is a **list of questions** you may address when evaluating the article.

1. What additional data should the authors have collected?

2. Did the methods generate results that would occur under natural field conditions? Why or why not? If not, how could the methods be changed to generate results that are more likely to occur in nature?

3. What could the authors have done to improve the quality of their publication?

4. Do the authors make any underlying assumptions? If so, what are they?

5. After reading this article, what questions remain unanswered?

6. Does this article stimulate any ideas for future research? If so, what are your ideas?

APPENDIX 1.
METRIC MEASUREMENT

The metric system (meters, liters, grams) is widely used throughout the world. The United States may be the only industrialized country that does not use the metric system as its main system of measurement. The First Congress, meeting in 1789, actually considered adopting a decimal system proposed by Thomas Jefferson, but ultimately took no action. The metric system originated in France in 1780, only a few years after Jefferson's proposal. Congress legalized the use of the new system for purposes of trade, but the English system (foot, ounce, and pound) was still predominant as it is today. A number of Congressional studies have been completed and laws passed either encouraging or requiring certain segments of the government to use the metric system. For example, President George H. W. Bush in 1991 signed an executive order (#12770) which directed all executive departments and federal agencies to implement the use of the metric system. School systems routinely teach the metric system, but most students fail to use it. As of January 2010, all products sold in the European Union were required to have only metric units on their labels. The U.S. has received an exemption to this requirement, but If we had not, what effect would that have had on products produced in this country?

In science, metric units are used exclusively. Therefore, this class will also only use metric units, and that includes using the Celsius system of measuring temperatures. When you make measurements in the laboratory you will use these units. The naming system, standard abbreviations, and conversion factors in Table 1 below will jog your memory.

Table 1. Metric units, abbreviations and conversion factors.

Distance		Volume		Mass	
meter	m	liter	L	gram	g
millimeter	mm	milliliter	ml	milligram	mg
centimeter	cm			kilogram	kg

Factor				Prefix		
One million	=	10^6	=	mega	=	M
One thousand	=	10^3	=	kilo	=	K
One hundred	=	10^2	=	hecto	=	h
One	=	10^0				
One–tenth	=	10^{-1}	=	deci	=	d
One–hundredth	=	10^{-2}	=	centi	=	c
One–thousandth	=	10^{-3}	=	milli	=	m
One–millionth	=	10^{-6}	=	micro	=	μ
One–billionth	=	10^{-9}	=	nano	=	n

Conversion Factors

1 inch	=	2.54 cm		1 centimeter	=	0.397 inch
1 yard	=	0.9144 m		1 meter	=	3.281 feet
1 mile	=	1.609 km		1 kilometer	=	0.6214 mile
1 ounce (dry)	=	28.35 grams		1 gram	=	0.035 ounce (dry)
1 pound	=	0.4536 kg		1 kilogram	=	2.205 pounds
1 ounce (fld)	=	29.57 ml		1 milliliter	=	0.034 ounces
1 quart	=	0.946 L		1 liter	=	1.0567 quarts

For Temperature

$$°F = (°C \times 1.8) + 32 \qquad °C = (°F - 32) \times 0.56$$

°F = degrees in Fahrenheit;   °C = degrees in Celsius

Use the *left* formula if you know the temperature in °C and want to convert it to °F. Use the *right* formula if you know the temperature in °F and want to convert it to °C.

The boiling temperature of water is 212 °F, and 100°C. The freezing point of water is 32°F and 0.0°C.

APPENDIX 2. HOW TO WRITE A LAB REPORT AND PRESENT AN ORAL REPORT

I. The Written Lab Report

The laboratory report **REQUIRES the following sections where each section must be TITLED as indicated.** But first, **TITLE the paper** and put your name and date on it. Do this on a Title Page. Please **double space** all sections, except the Literature Cited section which is to be single spaced. Please use a 12 point font and 1.0 inch margins.

INTRODUCTION (use this section title in your report)

Here you are to write about the **purpose** of the laboratory exercise. Why are we doing this exercise? Be specific about stating the purpose. In addition, why is doing what you did important or relevant to biology? Use your textbook (not the lab exercise) or another source to read about your area of study. Then, use some of that information to support what you write. Be **SURE** also to include your **hypotheses** in this section. You <u>must</u> construct **specific hypotheses** relating to this area of study and state them here. The hypotheses must be fairly specific. They should state a specific outcome rather than a general result.

In summary, the Introduction is your chance to:

1. tell the goals of your research,
2. lay out some background, and then
3. specify your hypotheses.

METHODS AND MATERIALS (use this section title in your report)

Here you tell the reader precisely what it was you did and how you did it. The description here should be specific enough so that anyone could set up and do your experiments based only on your directions. But, you do not need minute detail like the size of the beakers or that you used a ruler.

RESULTS (use this section title in your report)

The data generated during lab are the results: the filled-in data tables. But <u>from</u> the tables you will probably need to generate Figures (we don't call them graphs or charts and neither should you) which illustrate the results more clearly. If you do that, you do not need to include the data tables (raw data) in the report but **only** if all the data is presented in your figures. You should remember that a "table" consists of rows of numbers, while a "figure" is a graph or picture. Then, **number** all figures and tables and refer to them in your paper by their number. Don't forget that each figure must also have each **axis labeled** clearly. Also, **each line in each figure** must be identified by name within the figure preferably <u>**on the line itself**</u> **or in a legend** near the figure. In addition, be sure to <u>label each axis</u> <u>with the appropriate units</u> (are the numbers on the side grams? milliliters?).   Remember to give each figure or table you make a **title**: such as "Figure 1. The effect of temperature on CO_2 production by yeast." The title of each figure or table must have enough specificity so that the reader of your report will know what you have done. Remember, each figure or table must be able to stand on its own. That means that the reader should not have to look elsewhere in the report to figure out what the figure or table represents. Then (still in this section) **describe the data trends seen in those figures and tables using actual words**. This is a **required** narrative. Write things like "Figure 1 shows that ...., while Figure 2 demonstrates........." **Use some real numbers** from the figures to describe the data trends; **avoid only using terms like "more" or "less"** to describe data trends. However, do not think you have to write about each data point. Two or three well crafted sentences about each figure or table should be adequate.   A results section that only contains the words: "See results in Figures 1-3 and Table 1" or has no narrative is <u>not acceptable</u>.   When describing results, pretend that you are describing the figures and tables to a blind person (how can you make that person understand what has happened?).

In summary, the Results section presents the actual data generated (all of it), and through a written narrative tells what the data trends are for each figure and/or table. Here, you do not need to spend time telling why you think the results came out the way they did; that will be your job in the next section.

DISCUSSION (use this section title in your report)

Here you explain **what you think those data trends you found in the results mean**. What is the significance of the fact that (for example--not real trend) Figure 1 and Figure 4 had lines (trends) that ran in opposite directions? Address <u>why</u> the trends you see within the results came out the way they did. You need to look at all your data and see what it tells you. How do those results fit in with your understanding of the underlying biological principles? Note that you should refer back to at least some of the results in a direct fashion by using some **actual numbers**. Most descriptive statistics that you use should also be part of this section.

This section is probably the hardest to write because you have to apply the biological principles. Obviously, you must first understand them. **A Discussion section that does not include biological explanations of data trends derived from your references is doomed!** You must **integrate** the biological explanations into your discussion using the data trends to illustrate how the principles affected or shaped your results. This section is the most important and **will usually be looked at most closely for grading purposes**. Again, try to use some of the actual data in your explanation. Say things like: "The mean value (17.0 ml) for yeast at 10°C in Figure 1 shows that....." Also<u> be sure</u> to **revisit your initial hypotheses** and say whether you <u>accepted</u> or <u>rejected</u> them and why. But, we don't say that we proved or disproved a hypothesis.

The questions within the lab exercises are not to be turned in. **Instead**, incorporate or meld the answers to the questions into the Discussion. The things the questions ask about are typically things you need to address in the discussion since they relate directly to biological relevance.

In summary, use this section to address your hypotheses and explain **why** you think the results came out the way they did. Relate that explanation to biological principles. **Be sure** to address your original hypotheses and say whether you accepted them or rejected them (but **not** that you proved them or disproved them) and why. You may also include discussion of any problems that occurred during data collection that you feel may have affected the results, and any improvements to the methods that you think are appropriate. However, do not think that this latter type of discussion should comprise the bulk of the Discussion section.

LITERATURE CITED (use this section title in your report and not References or Works Cited)

Produce an alphabetical list (by author's last name) of any reference material used. Each reference citation must be complete. You **must have _____ references.** Your instructor will specify the number and type of references that are appropriate for the lab exercise. **The laboratory exercise itself is not an appropriate reference.** If you use a web site as a reference, **be sure** to include the **complete web address** of the document you read on line. References must be of sufficient quality for use in a college paper, and not, for example, a report from a student web site, on line encyclopedia or other low level source. It is safest to use sources whose urls include .edu or .gov. See Appendix 3 for more information about finding appropriate references.

In the body of the text, cite these references as follows: "Jones (2011) found that......", or "Raising the temperature is known to increase the rates of chemical reactions (Jones 2011)." Use only author(s) and the date, not page numbers. Also, note that the date must be placed immediately next to the author(s) name. Other systems of citing references are not acceptable including the use of foot notes or numbers. If the author is not printed, cite by using the following format (example follows): Anonymous, 2013.

In the Literature Cited section, **full reference citations must be used**. The citations themselves must be single spaced, but double space between citations.

Here is the format to be used in this section. Be sure to follow it.

If the reference source is a **book**:

Sagan, C. 1996. The demon-haunted world: science as a candle in the dark. New York: Random House. 470 p. (Note that the "470" is the total number of pages in the book; don't try to specify the particular pages you read).

If the reference is a **journal**:

> Berg, E. C. 2005. Parentage and reproductive success in the white-throated magpie-jay, *Calocitta formosa*, a cooperative breeder with female helpers. Animal Behavior, 70(2): 375–385. (Note: the "70" is the volume, the "(2)" is the volume part, and the "375–385" details the number of the first and last page in the article and <u>not</u> the specific page or pages you used).

If the reference is an article in a **newspaper**:

> Glaberson, W. 1999. The courts vs. scientific certainty. New York Times, June 7, Section 4 (column 3).

If the reference is an **internet source** (this means that the source did not appear first in a book or journal or newspaper):

> Derian, J. D. 1997. The US army fights tomorrow's war today. Wired (Online) 2 (9). Available from http://www.wired.com/Etext/index.html. (Note: you must include the specific web address that would take a person directly to the article and not simply "wired.com"; the "2 (9)" in this citation represents volume and part number, but many internet sources will not have this designation). Again, if the author is unknown, use "Anonymous" in place of the author's name.

Lastly, your instructor may have modifications for these guidelines, so please pay attention to specific instructions that may be given in class.

II. ORAL REPORTS

Oral reports provide the opportunity for you to communicate directly with your peers and the laboratory instructor about your work. Preparing for such reports can affect your nerves, but please realize that everyone is in the same situation. In addition, nervousness will not count against you for any grading purposes. The key to overcoming nervous reactions is to be prepared. Have good notes and also be sure to practice your presentation. It is not good to actually read your notes or power point slides. Instead, practice explaining what happened as if you are telling a story. Try to make it interesting. Never start a report by saying things like: "....well, I didn't much like this boring topic, and besides, our results didn't show anything...." Any time you give an oral report you should try to be positive and interesting, even if things did not turn out well. Believe it or not, the more oral presentations you give, the better you will be. Practice and experience enhances everything a person does. So, make sure your group practices the entire presentation prior to actually giving your report.

The order of the topics of your report will be the same as in the written report. Since there will be about four people in each group, it is up to the group to decide who will do which part. Also, longer report sections can be divided up between two people. You may wish to develop a power point presentation, but that is not necessarily required. The use of over heads (your instructor can make them quickly for you) or, for example, EXCEL or WORD figures and tables from a computer to the video projector are also acceptable. But no matter which system you use, be sure that the class will be able to view the results and data analyses clearly. It will be necessary to show your results (figures and tables) and then discuss the trends. Oral only presentations of results are not appropriated for this class.

Lastly, be ready for questions. Other students in the class will be encouraged to ask questions and your instructor may also have a few questions. Knowing your topic is the best defense or preparation for questions. It is also a good idea for the members of your group to grill each other as a practice mechanism.

APPENDIX 3. FINDING ACADEMIC RESOURCES

Locating the proper kind of resources to use in papers you write is not always easy. One quick way to get lots of stuff is to google your topic. This internet search engine will typically return hundreds, thousands, or even millions of sources. For example, when the search term "diffusion" was used (will be covered in lab) Google returned over 128 <u>million</u> sources! One of the problems here is that most of the sources returned are useless for writing a college paper. "But it's on line, it must be OK…" many will say. Not so. Many of the sources are really not authoritative; that is, they were not produced by real experts, so college professors in every department will disallow their use. How can you find acceptable reference materials? The answer will vary depending on the subject matter, on the level of your course, and on your particular professors, who will have their own ideas about this to which you will need to pay attention.

The best place to start is at CNU's Trible Library. You can access the library's home page at **cnu.edu/library**. From there you can find books, articles, and electronic resources on your topic. The <u>Online Catalog</u> is accessed by clicking on "**Library Catalog**" in the box on the left side of the home page. You can also go directly to the Online Catalog by going to **read.cnu.edu**. Once you are there you can search using keywords or other kinds of search terms. Your search will return books and journals available in the library and some online resources. Of course, to use books, journals (we don't call them magazines) and other resources in the library you may have to actually get on your feet and walk on over. Once you are actually at the Library you can ask the reference librarian on duty if you need help finding or using the resources.

You can also access **electronic indexes**, which will provide gateways to many thousands of relevant, professionally written articles and books. Some of those articles you can then directly download ("full text articles" or "pdf"). Others, which supply an abstract only, you might have to send away for using the Library's Interlibrary Loan mechanism (click on "Interlibrary Loan" on the left side of the homepage). The electronic indexes or databases that are available are accessed by clicking on "Databases A to Z" on the left of the Library's home page. The indexes that are especially appropriate for Biology include Biological

Sciences, Biological Journals (Proquest), BioOne, Cambridge Journals Environmental Sciences & Pollution Management, First Search, JSTOR, New York Times (1851–2011), Proquest Online, Proquest Science & Technology and SciFinder Scholar. Additional online resources are available through the CNU website by clicking on "**Databases A–Z**" at the left side of the library's home page. These links contain hundreds of databases and thousands of full text journals of all types, not just Biology. Take a look and be prepared to spend some time looking around. Again, be sure to check with your instructor about which individual sources are deemed acceptable. But please, lose the habit of using encyclopedias whether or not they are online or in paper. At the college level, you need to learn to go to the source of the information, and that will not be encyclopedias or general web site information.

Another online source (but not directly through our library) is Google Scholar (**scholar.google.com**). This search engine provides access to thousands of scholarly publications. Some are full text, others are abstracts only. Google Scholar, though, is not comprehensive even though most searches will return dozens, hundreds, or even thousands of sources. Of course, the utility of the sources depends on the search terms you use. Learning how to develop search terms for Google or any other electronic indexes will take some time. Most students start out too broad ("animals"), but quickly learn that such general terms return too many useless sources. Instead, think carefully about your topic and try to be more specific ("dolphin physiology," or "diving physiology dolphins"). Don't worry if you have to try three or four times.

It may take awhile to find what you need, and then even more time to read and understand what you read. **Give yourself the time**; don't procrastinate. Ask questions of your lab instructor if you are not sure about what it is you have read or if you are having trouble developing search terms that work well. And don't forget that you can actually walk over to the Library and consult face-to-face with the reference librarian on duty. You can also contact the librarians by clicking on "**Get Help**" on the homepage. This includes an online chat service.

The expectations present in a college environment for quality of resources is different than in high school. Don't get discouraged if you initially have some problems. Learning how to find and use appropriate academic resources is both a science and an art which will improve, like everything else, with practice.

APPENDIX 4. DATA ANALYSIS

Generating data is easy in a laboratory setting. It is harder to know what to do with it. How can you best analyze that data so that you can better judge the results of your work? Scientists, as you know, make observations about the natural world. "Leaves are green" might be one of them. If they want to carry things further, they create and test a hypothesis, like "Leaves on trees are greener in the middle of a forest than at the edges of the forest." Next, they must find a way to measure leaf color and then use that technique on numerous leaves at both the forest center and forest edge. They would be doing a "survey."   However, it is unlikely that all the measurements in any one location will be the same. This would be due to natural variation and also sampling error (yes, even scientists can make mistakes). So, if you have a string of data points from the two locations, you need to know the proper techniques for comparing that data so that you can address your hypothesis. Typically, when comparing data from two surveys (like the leaf example) or experimental treatments in a lab, the two strings of data points will "look" different. But how different do they have to be for you to conclude that the data are **significantly** different? This is where statistical analysis comes in.

Statistics is an important tool for scientists or anyone trying to analyze data. Students who major in Biology, Psychology, Sociology, Business and other disciplines will be required to complete a course in statistics. Bottom line is that one has to know **what** to do with information that you generate in data form, and **how** to interpret the work of others who have used statistical analysis. In this class, you will learn to use EXCEL 2010 to calculate simple statistical values such as the mean, standard deviation, and variance and to conduct simple statistical tests like the "t-test" and linear correlation.

For example, you have gathered data on hand spans. The following procedures will lead you through the methods necessary to calculate simple statistics from your data, and also teach you to do a **t-test**, whose results will allow you to determine whether or not the mean values of the hand spans, or any data comparison you wish to make, are significantly different from each other. In the following example, we will use the data generated from male and female hand spans. We will hypothesize that "male hand spans are no different from female hand spans." This is a "**null" hypothesis**, meaning that you are expecting no difference in the results. On the way to addressing this hypothesis, you will learn how to utilize EXCEL to calculate simple statistics and to do a t-test.

I. ANALYSIS OF HAND SPAN DATA USING SIMPLE STATISTICS

The first lab exercise that will generate data is the exercise that includes hand span analysis. You will use some of the data generated in that lab to learn how to produce usable statistics. Please realize that while there are a lot of steps here, after you do this the first time, you will be able to do the next analysis in just a few minutes.

PROCEDURES

1. Do one of the following:

a. Open EXCEL and type "Male" at the top of column 1, and "Female" at the top of column 2. These are labels for your data. Then enter the data for hand span in the appropriate column, OR

b. Open in EXCEL the data file generated in class.

2. You will next generate basic, descriptive statistics from these data. These types of statistics are commonly used and are probably somewhat familiar to you. They include
   –the **mean** (an arithmetic average),
   –the **variance** (a measure of the dispersion of a set of data points around the mean),
   –the **standard deviation** (another method to measure the spread of data where 68% of all data is always within one standard deviation, 95% of all data is always within two standard deviations; this goes for any data set; the standard deviation is actually determined by taking the positive square root of the variance),
   –the **range** (the number of units from the lowest data point value to the highest data point value which is typically expressed by stating the lowest data point followed by the highest data point: for example, 17–33, and
   –other statistics like the median, minimum, maximum, sum and count will also be calculated.
3. In order to calculate all of these descriptive statistics for your data, put the cursor in a blank cell in your worksheet. This will be where the calculated values will be placed. Now click on the "Data" button at the top of the spread sheet. A list spread

across the top of the spreadsheet will open. If you are using your personal computer and the list does **not** include "Data Analysis" then follow the instructions in the text box below.   If the list <u>does</u> include "Data Analysis" then click on it and highlight "Descriptive Statistics." Now click the "OK" button. The Descriptive Statistic box will

---

The instructions in this text box are for use on your own personal computer which is running Office 2010. If you are using other versions, then you can find specific instructions via the Help menu. In lab, the Data Analysis pack has been preloaded. If the Data Analysis line does NOT appear on the list in your computer, you must install it by first clicking on "File" on the top-left. Then click on "Options" and then click on "Add-Ins" on the left. In the "Add-Ins Available" box select "Analysis ToolPak" and then click "OK." This will load the Data Analysis pack, though you may be prompted to insert the original EXCEL disk to complete the task. At this point if you see a message that the Analysis ToolPak is not currently installed, click "Yes" to install it. Now the Data Analysis command is available in the "Analysis" group on the "Data" tab at the top of the page in Excel.

---

open. Make sure that the "Summary Statistics" box is checked. If you have labeled the data columns ("male" and "female"), then check the box next to "Labels in First Row," which tells the program that the first row does not contain numbers. Next, activate the "Input Range" by clicking the icon at the right end of the Input Range window. Now highlight the data in both columns by clicking and dragging (<u>highlight data only</u>, not the labels in the first row). This should result in a running dotted line which surrounds all your data. Click that same icon button to restore the full window. Next, check "Output Range" and click on the icon at its right in order to tell the program where exactly you want the summary statistics to appear on your spreadsheet. In order to do this, first click on an empty cell in your spreadsheet. Click on the icon on the right to restore the full window. Finally, click on "OK"   The newly calculated summary statistics will now appear on your data sheet in table form. Check a few of the numbers to make sure that you highlighted the data columns correctly during this process.

But suppose you <u>only</u> want to calculate the mean or average. You can do individual functions, the average or other single statistics, as follows. First click on the cell just below the column of numbers with which you are working. Now look just above the data columns and find a small **Function** button (ƒx). Click on it and a box labeled "Insert Functions" will open up. To do any of the listed operations choose the operation to be done and then click on the "OK" box. When you do this, another box, the "Function Argument" box opens. Notice that your column of figures is specified in the window labeled 'Number 1'. Click OK and the calculated value now appears in the previously selected cell. Repeat for all functions desired. Be sure to **label** these calculated values if you want to keep track of them. In EXCEL, there are several ways to approach various methods of analysis.

II. COMPARING TWO DATA SETS

We considered, earlier, the hand span data sets from males and females. We could calculate the means of the two data sets, which are probably different. But are they different enough to say that we can reject the <u>hypothesis that male hand spans are no different from female hand spans</u>? How much of a difference does it take? You really cannot determine this by calculating the means alone or eyeballing all the numbers. In the world of science, we use statistical tests to tell us whether one data set is **significantly** different from another data set. The use of the word "significantly" has statistical implications in the sciences and should not be used casually. Of course, even with these statistical tests, there is still a chance of error as you will see.

A. T TEST

One statistical test that can be done is a **t-test** (lower case "t") to see if these means are statistically (and significantly) different. But first, we first have to see if the variability of the two sets of data is basically equal or very different. That is, we must do an **F-test**. We do this because if the variability of the two data sets is very different, then we must use a different kind of t-test to analyze whether or not the means are the same or significantly different.

PROCEDURES

1. The assumption now is that you have an open EXCEL data sheet with two columns of data, one labeled "Male" and one labeled "Female." Of course, you can do these operations with most data sets.

2. Click on the "Data" button at the top of the screen and select **DATA ANALYSIS** at the end of the banner. Then choose **F-test Two-Sample for Variances** and click on "OK." Running this test will tell you what kind of t-test to use on your data (yes, there is more than one kind of t test!).

3. Fill the necessary information in the F-test box as follows: activate the "**variable 1 range**" window by placing the cursor in this window, and then highlight the range containing these values <u>including the label</u> by clicking and dragging. Do the same for the "**variable 2 range**" window. Click once in the square marked "**Labels**" so that a checkmark (✓) appears, and use an **alpha level** of **0.05** which is specified just below the "Labels" box. This allows us a 5% margin of error which is a standard often used within science for such tests.

4. Click in the circle marked "**output range**," and activate the window next to this. Then highlight an empty cell making sure that there are empty cells to the right and below it. This is where the **F-test results** will appear. Click "**OK**" which will generate the results.

5. The results will allow you to know whether or not the variances of the two data sets are equal. If your calculated F value ("F" in the box) is greater than the critical F value ("F Critical" in box), then the variances are not equal. If the calculated F is less than or equal to the critical F value, variances are equal.

6. Based on the results of this F test, you can now use a **t-test** to determine if there is a statistically significant difference between the means. To do this test, click on the Data button at the top of the page and then click on **DATA ANALYSIS** at the right of the screen. Then **choose the correct t-test to use based upon the results of the F-test**.

7. If the F test found unequal variances, then choose "t-Test: Two Sample Assuming Unequal Variances." If the F test found that the variances were basically the same, then choose: "t-Test: Two-Sample Assuming Equal Variances."

8. You will do this statistical test the same way you did the F test. You can use the same methods as outlined in steps 3 and 4 (above). You can now address your hypothesis ("There is no difference between male and female hand span mean lengths" – the null hypothesis). You interpret the results of the t-test in the same way you did the F-test, where you **reject** your hypothesis if the your calculated t value ("t Stat") is greater than the critical t value (use "t Critical two tail" at the bottom of the box), and **accept** your hypothesis if the calculated t value is less than or equal to the critical t value. Your t stat may come out as a negative number, but ignore the minus sign if that happens—all calculated t stats are considered to be positive. Also, you may need to expand a column if you cannot read everything in the results box. Remember, again, that with this test you are assessing the null hypothesis ("...there is no difference in the means of the data sets..."). So, in the introduction of your report, you must state your hypotheses accordingly ("I hypothesize that there is no difference in mean hand spans between......")

If your calculated t statistic is negative, IGNORE that minus sign. All calculated t statistics must be expressed as positive numbers.

B. CORRELATION

Sometimes we want to know to what extent two variables increase or decrease with each other in a straight line relationship. For example, we might think that if height increases in a data set, then hand span also increases. That is, we think that height and hand span are *correlated* with each other. We could, and probably should, graph the results to see what they look like. The figure would show two lines, one representing height and the other hand span. If hand span increases are accompanied with height increases, we might say that there is a **positive correlation** between the two. If hand span **decreases** as height **increases**, we would say that there is a **negative correlation** between the two. But if there appears to be no relationship and the lines on the graph crisscross several times, we would say that there is **no correlation** between these factors.

> **Correlation**: A measure of the mutual relationship between two variables. The correlation coefficient, "r," ranges from -1.0 to +1.0. A -1.0 indicates a strong negative correlation, +1.0 indicates a strong positive correlation, and 0.0 or around 0.0 indicates that there is no correlation between the two factors being considered.

In science, we must do more than only look at the character of the data lines. In science, we need to actually calculate the correlation coefficient. Once calculated, the formula produces a number ranging from −1.0 to +1.0. If the coefficient is a **positive** number then that is a "positive correlation" indicating that as one factor increases, so does the other factor. The closer the coefficient is to +1.0 the stronger is the claim. If the coefficient is a **negative** number, then that is a "negative correlation" meaning that as one set of values increases, the other set of values decreases. The closer the negative coefficient is to −1.0, the stronger is the claim. But what if the coefficient is **zero or close to zero** (neither very positive nor very negative)? If that were the case, we would say that there is "no correlation" between the factors.

Here is how to calculate a correlation coefficient for your data using EXCEL. This is really VERY easy to do.

PROCEDURES

1. Open your EXCEL data sheet as you did when performing the t test. You will have two columns of data, one labeled (for this example) "height" and one labeled "hand span."

2. Click on "Data" at the top of the screen and then click on "Data Analysis" at the right. Now click on "Correlation" and then click "OK" at the right side of the box.

3. A dialog box will open. As before when calculating other statistics, you must indicate the "Input Range" (click and drag to highlight **both** columns of numbers **with labels**) and then click on "Labels in First Row."

4. The only thing you need to do now is make sure that the "Output Range" is on an empty cell, one that has no data. The output range might look something like this: A25, which tells you that the correlation coefficient, once calculated, will be placed in column A, row 25. If this cell has data in it, then you must change this range. To change the output range, highlight the range in the dialog box and then click on an empty cell in your spreadsheet.

5. Now click **OK** in the dialog box and immediately you will see the correlation coefficient appear in the selected spot on the spreadsheet.

6. Ignore the 1.0 value (where the two variables are tested against themselves which always produces a perfect 1.0 correlation) and use the other number generated at the confluence of the height and hand span column and row.

III. MAKING FREQUENCY HISTOGRAMS WITH EXCEL

A good way to present your data is to construct a figure (chart or graph, as many call it). Figures like bar graphs or line graphs illustrate the data. It is easier to generally interpret results if the results are graphically presented. Then, you don't have to really spend time reading the data, because you can easily see the trends since what you are looking at is, in essence, a picture. Using the hand span data, a method will be described which will allow you to present the number of individuals in defined categories and then to use these values to create a figure. That is, you will create a graphic representation of your data.

PROCEDURES

1. Open or create the Hand Span data file on an Excel data sheet.

2. This data sheet should have three columns: hand span widths (the "bins," as Excel calls them), male measurements, and female measurements.

3. These data <u>must be in order</u>. For example, if hand spans range from a low of 15 cm to a high of 24 cm, then your measurements, or bins, must start at 15 cm at

the top of the column and run down the various hand span categories with 24 at the bottom.

4. opposite each bin number (the hand span widths in the first column), you will enter the frequency or number of males with that hand span (column 2) and then the number of females with that hand span (column 3). Continue filling in the table until all data is entered (in this example, down through bin 24).

5. Now highlight columns 2 and 3 (click and drag—**including the labels** (male and female) at the top.

6. Next, click on **Insert** at the top of the page. A new banner will open up. Then click on **column** and then click on **2-D Column** and immediately your data will be graphed. As you probably noticed, after clicking on column, a whole variety of possible chart types appear. You could use any of them, but for now, use the first 2-D column.

7. The figure that appears is a bar graph showing the frequency of male and female hand spans for each bin item or hand span width. But, the horizontal or x axis does not show the bins associated with the frequencies of male and female data. This is easily corrected.

8. Right click on the x or horizontal axis (where the numbers are located on the very bottom of the figure). A box will open. Now click on **select data**. A new box will open that, in turn, is partitioned into two boxes. Use the right box labeled "horizontal (category) axis labels." Click on **edit** and then a new window will open. Click on the icon that looks like a tiny Excel screen at the right end of open skinny, box. Now highlight (click and drag) the mouse pointer over the contents of column 1 of your data list. This is the bin column with the categories of hand span widths. Only highlight the numbers in this column.

9. Click on **OK**, then on **OK** again. Now your figure shows your data associated with the proper hand span widths.

10. You can add a title to the chart by doing the following. First click anywhere in the chart. A "Chart Tools" box will open up at the top of the screen. Now click on the "Layout" tab on the line just below the Chart Tools box. Then click on the "Chart Titles" tab and then on "Centered Overlay Title." A text box then will appears in your

figure with the words "Chart Title". Click on that text box and replace "Chart Title" with an appropriate title (for example, "Fig. 1. Distribution of hand span widths in males and females").

11. You can **label** the horizontal and vertical axes in a similar fashion. Click anywhere in the figure so that "Chart Tools" appears at the top of the screen. Then click on "Axis Titles" just below the words "Chart Tools." Click on "Axis Titles" and choose which axis you want to label ("primary horizontal axis title" or "primary vertical axis title"). A secondary box will open allowing you to direct the text box/axis title to the appropriate spot. Click on that and, as before when constructing the figure title, a text box will appear within your figure. Click on that new text box and create a descriptive title for the axis you chose. Then repeat the process for the other axis.

12. There are many, many options available in Excel for making and adjusting charts or figures, and if you have additional questions about modification, click on the question mark icon at the top right of the screen.

13. Voila!! You have a histogram of your hand span data in only 10 steps (give or take)!!! Actually, once you have done this one time, you will be able to move quickly through these procedures in five to ten minutes.

The above-created figure can be printed directly or copied into Word to be part of a larger report. Use the COPY and PASTE functions to do this.

APPENDIX 5. USING MICROSCOPES

Before the discovery of lens systems in the 16th century, biologists were unable to observe organisms and cellular structure that were beyond the normal range of vision. This limited their knowledge and understanding. When the microscope was invented, scientists were finally able to observe not only small (micro) creatures, but fine details of organisms and cells. Once they saw those things, they were then compelled to study them and explain their function. So, microscopes are tools that are used by biologists to get a closer look at whole creatures (if they are small), whole parts of creatures, and thin slices of creatures. See the text box for additional information on the history of lenses leading to microscopes.

The microscopes you will use in lab include the compound microscope and the dissecting microscope. The **compound microscope**, Figure 1, is used to examine tiny pieces of creatures or tiny aquatic creatures where the specimen is placed on a glass slide, a drop or two of water is added, and then a cover slip is placed on top. The specimen must be transparent enough to allow light to pass through it. If the specimen is too thick the field of view will be dark. This microscope, therefore, relies on *transmitted* light. The **dissecting microscope**, Figure 2, can be used to examine anything that can fit on the stage ranging from your hand, to snail shells, to thick slide preparations. Typically, light used to operate this microscope bounces off the top of the specimen and then through the microscope to your eyes (*reflected* light.

HERE ARE A FEW RULES. Always handle microscopes carefully. Carry them with two hands and gently place them on the lab tables. Be sure not to bump them against objects, and clean them quickly and thoroughly if anything is spilled on them. **Lens paper must be used when cleaning the lenses** of the microscope, which are located in the eyepieces and the objectives. Paper towels may be used when cleaning other parts of the microscope. If you use glass slides, be sure to wash and dry them and return them to their box. Cover slips are disposable.

Using a microscope is not difficult, but like all things it takes some practice. Learning the names of the main parts of the microscope and their functions is necessary for efficient use. This link will allow you to practice using the digital microscope:

http://tinyurl.com/lqgoq5c

Read the information on the opening page and then click on "**the virtual scope**" on the third line to get started. This will take no more than 10–15 minutes and will help.

Figure 1. Compound microscope.

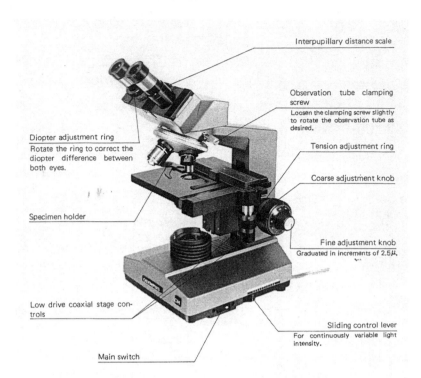

Figure 2. Dissecting microscope.

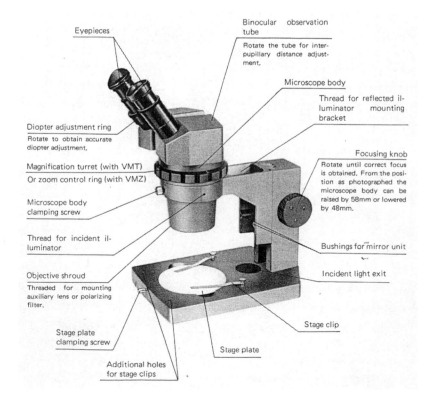

A Short History of Lens Use

14th Century. The art of grinding lenses was developed in Italy and "spectacles" were first manufactured to improve vision.

1590. Dutch lens grinders Hans and Zacharias Janssen constructed the first microscope by placing two lenses in a tube.

1667. Robert Hooke used a microscope to describe the tiny objects that make cork float (i.e. he discovered cells).

1675. Anton van Leeuwenhoek published extensive descriptions he made of blood, insects, bacteria and other cells using a microscope with only one lens.

18th and 19th Century. Many improvements were made to microscopes making them easier to use and more popular among scientists. The system of using weak lenses placed together to produce high power, clear images was developed by Joseph Jackson Lister in 1830.

20th Century. Richard Zsigmondy (1903) developed the ultramicroscope which was used to study objects below the wavelength of light (Nobel prize, 1925). The phase contrast microscope, used to study transparent objects, was developed by Frits Zernike in 1932 (Nobel prize, 1953). The electron microscope was invented by Ernst Ruska in 1938, which used electron beams rather than light (Nobel prize, 1986). The scanning tunneling microscope which gives three-dimensional images down to atomic level was invented in 1981 by Gerd Binnig and Heinrich Rohrer (Nobel prize, 1986).

2000. The invention of structured illumination microscopy (SIM) revolutionized high-resolution optical imaging by shining patterned light on a subject from different angles and then using computer algorithms to extract information from the resulting fringe patterns to produce high-resolution images, doubled the resolution possible using conventional optics.

APPENDIX 6. URLs AND QRs LISTED BY EXERCISE NUMBER

Exercise 1. Introduction to the Biological Sciences

http://tinyurl.com/ocnc6gy

http://tinyurl.com/qzonavq

Exercise 2. Hands on Variation

http://tinyurl.com/nv529uq

http://www.dnaftb.org

Exercise 3. Sweating, Sports Drinks and Biology

http://tinyurl.com/osmkoeq

http://tinyurl.com/yzaqfq

http://tinyurl.com/c6jsgem

http://tinyurl.com/qammqjy

http://tinyurl.com/42by8e   http://tinyurl.com/5wn3kw

Exercise 4. Evolution and Snails

http://tinyurl.com/88554    http://tinyurl.com/yamntj

http://tinyurl.com/ndhdsyv   http://tinyurl.com/qjl2r4r

Exercise 5. Science and Wine

http://tinyurl.com/6uh6z8t    http://tinyurl.com/8294jtb

Exercise 6. Ecology: Nutrient Pollution

http://tinyurl.com/puhlaxn   http://tinyurl.com/omfq7dj